Also available from Unsung Stories
Déjà Vu by Ian Hocking
The Beauty by Aliya Whiteley

DARK STAR

OLIVER LANGMEAD

UNSUNG
STORIES

Published by Unsung Stories, an imprint of Red Squirrel Publishing
Red Squirrel is a registered trademark of Shoreditch Media Limited

Red Squirrel Publishing
Suite 235, 77 Beak Street, London W1F 9DB, United Kingdom

www.unsungstories.co.uk

First published in 2015 – First impression

Cover Artwork © 2015 Carolina Rodriguez Fuenmayor
Interior Illustration © 2015 Darren Kerrigan

Paperback ISBN: 978-1-907389-30-6
ePub ISBN: 978-1-907389-31-3

Editor: George Sandison
Editorial Assistant: Suzanne Connelly
Copy Editor: Robert Sterling
Proofreader: Jennifer Wade
Designer: Martin Cox
Publisher: Henry Dillon

Printed in the UK by TJ International

PROLOGUE

Time to waste, so I escape the city
At one of those seedy establishments
They call 'Glow Shows' because they fill the girls
So full of Pro' it nearly burns their veins.

Prometheus, resident wonder-drug;
Pro', Promo', 'Theus, liquid-fucking-light;
Prohibited by city law and shot
By yours truly, Virgil Yorke, hero cop.

These moments, liquid light coursing through me,
Trickling across my veins in streams, feeling
Like fluttering fingers under my skin,
Are all that's left holding me together.

The girls move and I start to lose focus,
The needle forgotten in hand. I'm numb,
Forgetting my scar, forgetting it all,
Seeing blurs and shapes and losing myself.

There's a rhythm. It might be the music.
It might be the protesting of my heart
As it pushes light right into my head.
It could be anything for all I care.

   The girls are becoming hypnotic whirls,
The only thing here my eyes want to see.
Time stretches and folds and as I sink in
I realise it's not them I'm seeing.

   I'm staring at the only bulb in here,
The single hanging light they can afford,
Swinging lazy like a slow pendulum
And leaving lines streaked across my vision.

   Here's the high. I rise above the strip bar,
Above the building, above the city,
Past our hell, our nemesis, our dark sun,
Until I'm among the stars, surrounded.

   My body waits below, in the city,
Fingers twitching and pupils dilated,
The wrong side of dignified. Just for now,
I am free. Tomorrow can go to hell.

   Here, there's no noose around my neck, no scar
Where it bit my flesh, where it nearly killed—
Where it should have killed me. I have no weight
Up here. I can't drag myself down and choke.

❯ • ❮

Sleep. It feels so long since I last got sleep.
There are eighty-one steps. I count them all,
Treading careful in the dark over trash
And the maybe-dead: Vox's lightless ghosts.

There's a railing made rough by years of rust.
It snags at my fingers and takes me home.
I never bother to lock the front door.
There's nothing inside worth stealing. No light.

Here's my hole in the world. My patch of black.
The pit where I lay down my flesh and bones
And let them rest a while away from work.
There was a bulb once. It broke some time back.

It's quiet. There's a watch in here somewhere
And I can hear it tick, soft as rainfall.
I leave my coat near the door in a heap,
Shuffle out of my boots and feel bare wood.

If I don't keep my eyes open in here,
I'll sleep where I stand. This dark is okay,
Anyway. Full of the smell of whisky,
The smell of my papers, books and damp rot.

I shave around the scar across my throat,
Shower cold to keep awake and listen
To the pipes complain, to my stomach turn.
Last cycle's leftovers will have to do.

By the bottle's weight, I'd say it's half gone,
And the other half follows quick enough,
Swallowed urgent, like medicine; a cure
For the thump of my brain against my skull.

I collapse into a half-broken chair,
Reading by the tips of my fingers all
The news of half-broken Vox, dark city
Getting darker every minute passing.
  Somewhere between articles the whisky
Grabs me, forces my eyes shut, my head low,
Fingers paused on 'gallant' like it's a word
That might find use outside a newspaper.
  Here's oblivion, then. The dark inside
My head. I've half drowned myself in whisky,
But it's still not enough. I dream again.
This cycle's big comedown. Lower than low.
  'Stand on the tips of your toes,' he says soft,
Like he's teaching me how to dance. The noose
Is a coarse loop dividing me from me.
I can't see him, but I hear him. 'Right up.'

FIRST CYCLE

Dante drives the borrowed squad car direct.
He's an accident of flesh and blunt bones
Shaped human, ugly and mostly scowling,
Made bitter by the job and the city.

The car's engine coughs, groans loud and sounds sick,
Making the noises that mark how I am.
Here's this cycle's comedown, deserved of time
Spent pricked and dissolved into my habits.

Good old Dante pretends not to notice.
He watches the glinting out in the road,
Keeps us on course, wherever we're going.
The radio is coarse static chatter.

We don't talk much, and when we do it's bleak.
'Read the papers?' 'Yeah, more complaints, more strikes.'
'Vox is going to hell.' 'Just like ever.'
Words said between us feel kinda empty.

I wind down a window, let the rain in
And ignite a cigarette, dragging deep.
Dante accepts my offer, bends his head,
Lets me ignite his; nostrils hissing smoke.

'Like hell I know what this is about, Yorke.'
He grumbles from the corner of his mouth,
Lips tight. 'I'm sick of cleaning up hookers.'
The window leaks our warmth. It's refreshing.

I try to watch the city as we pass.
It's a big black bulk, always out of sight.
Feels like it might come down any cycle;
Collapse under its own overgrown weight.

There's a glint of something between buildings,
Some source of light left uncovered out there.
We pass and I can see the silhouettes
Of Vox's ghosts, the light-starved hunting glows.

That gone, there's only the rain seeping down
To see, lit up by the squad car's headlight.
The vague shape of the city surrounds us,
Just out of range of sight, hidden away.

Other cars pass, spraying rain in their wakes.
There's not many out. It's too hard to see.
We're only out here from necessity.
Orders from up high; orders to obey.

Dante cuts the car and the rain gets loud.
I meet his eye and he's glaring at me,
Chewing at the end of his cigarette.
'To hell with it,' he growls, pockets the keys.

He runs, hiding underneath a paper,
Raised pictures and text turned unreadable.
I follow, soaked the moment I step out,
Slow behind. No sense trying to fight it.

There's a man waiting, umbrella held high.
He's almost as wide as Dante, but tall,
Suit several sizes too small, seams bursting.
Behind him, there's some floodlights. Strange out here.

There's an exchange between him and Dante.
I'm too busy searching my coat to hear,
Trying to find just one dry cigarette.
Whole pack's gone. Great start to a great cycle.

'Shit, Yorke. You listening?' Dante's voice is loud,
Trying to be heard over the downpour.
'It's a DEA case. Someone's fucked up.'
The floodlights are way too bright. I squint, frown.

Our big friend looks like he's carved out of stone.
He thrusts a hand out at me, engulfs mine.
He's Drug Squad and I'm wary. I'm hoping
There's no Pro' afterglow beneath my skin.

'DC Fife.' 'DI Yorke. Why are we here?'
He raises an eyebrow. 'Yorke? I know you.
Seen you in the newspapers. Real good work.'
Can't escape my own damn reputation.

I shrug his words away. 'Why are we here?'
He takes my subtle hint. Gets to the point.
'We need your help and you're gonna need ours.
Cross-department case. Hell of a thing, too.'

Past parked cars, rope, a crowd of spectators,
Flaps of canvas keeping the sky's worst back.
There's a lot of men in heavy coats stood,
Taking notes, all unsure how to react.

She's a hell of a thing. Hell of a thing.
'Phos and fire, Yorke.' Dante steams and curses.
It's a dead-end back alley, filled up with
Garbage and, right now, a flood of bright light.

I was wrong to think that there were floodlights.
Nobody's got a torch lit. There's no need.
She's difficult to look at. She's too bright.
She's lighting the whole damn scene with her blood.

I suddenly need to smoke real urgent.
Dante offers up one of his, still dry;
Ignites it for me. I inhale and hold.
Neither of us can keep our eyes off her.

Her veins are alight, webbed under her skin;
Glowing eyes wide open, mouth leaking light.
She's something else. Like one of those cheap girls
Downtown, but intensified. Much brighter.

'Promo'?' Dante's glaring across at me.
I'm meant to be the expert between us,
But this is stupid. 'Only if someone
Took out all her blood first, filled her back up.'

Hard to tell what she looked like normally.
She's a mess of light, could be anyone.
It takes me a while to notice the warmth.
Girl's blood is giving off a lot of heat.

It's pooled all around her, thick and still wet.
My eyes slowly adjust to see better
How she's been killed. Looks like a gunshot wound
Punctured her heart, or somewhere near enough.

Our friend Fife steps in front, is an eclipse.
'Look,' he says. 'Cause of death could be the blood,
Could be the shot. We don't know. Hard to tell.
But 'til we do, we're all on this. Okay?'

I realise I haven't exhaled. 'Sure.'
Everyone's looking at me like I know
What to do next. How to deal with all this.
'Got an ID?' 'Yeah.' Fife fumbles around.

Dante reads through, gives me the short and sweet
While I get closer, look her up and down.
Her hands are clenched tight, arms still tense, rigid.
Looks like she might have died of fright alone.

'Vivian North,' grunts Dante. 'Girl can drive.
Owns a car. Ah Phos, Yorke. She's a student.'
The case just got important. Girl's wealthy;
It's hard to afford an education.

Hard to imagine her not full of light.
Fife's been here longer, I ask what he knows.
'Got a weapon?' 'No weapon. No nothing.'
Dead ends are fine. Less questions that need asked.

'How'd she get here?' My eyes begin to ache.
'No car parked up. We've asked around and found
Six witnesses that'll swear to a van,
But no one we'd like to pay for details.'

Vivian, tell me, how'd you end up here?
An uptown girl like you all the way down
With me, halfway between dark and darker,
Filled up with fright and blood so bright it burns;

So bright you've been burned into my vision.
I turn away and can still see you there.
Even when I close my eyes, there you are.
I must have pupils like pinheads right now.

'Who's in charge here?' Nobody meets my eye.
They all look like shades, like hunched-up shadows.
Fife is igniting a cigar, watching.
'Looks like you are,' grunts Dante, damn his hide.

Fife inhales deep, rolls the cigar around,
Leaking smoke. 'How do you want to do this?'
'I don't want to do this.' 'You're the hero.'
I stare at him straight. 'I'm no damn hero.'

Can't get the girl out of my vision now.
Can't blink her away. She's a white scarring.
I leave the tent, back out into the dark
And the rain, chewing on my cigarette.

Choosing to interpret my defiance
As acceptance, Dante gives some orders.
I can hear him shouting over the rain,
Can hear people moving with a purpose.

The dark is pleasant. The girl starts to fade.
'You're a fucking mess, Yorke.' Dante joins me.
I don't disagree, but I take off fast.
'Where are you going?' he calls. 'Straight to hell.'

'You can't walk out. This is your fucking case.'
We spread damp across the car seats, dry off.
I take a break, smoke some more and calm down.
We talk it through. Dante says what he's done.

'I got people looking for the girl's car.
Gave Fife the scene to babysit; wait up
For the coroner to go over it.
Which leaves us two things left to do, both bad.'

He's right. 'Both bad' doesn't cut it, either.
I sit and think and there's no easy way.
'We'll tell her folks first.' It's only polite.
'Then we'll check out the University.'

Leafing through papers, Dante finds a map,
Finds the place we gotta go. Way uptown.
'You drive,' I tell him. Can't keep my hands still.
Great time for tremors. I clench my fists tight.

We pull away and I can still see her.
She's only an outline now, barely there,
Like a backwards silhouette; white on black.
I close my eyes and try to keep them closed.

❯ • ❮

'I don't take it black.' 'You do right now, Yorke.'
We grab coffee. It's as hot as hellfire
But it gives me the kick I've been craving.
'You sure you're up to this? I'm serious.'

Dante is giving me the look he saves
For bad car-wrecks, like I'm a disaster.
Maybe he's right. Maybe I'm burned out. 'Sure.'
I drain the cup. 'Let's go break the bad news.'

> • <

We leave the looming bulk of the city,
Pass through gates, flash badges at uniforms,
And drive through my least favourite part of town.
Here the wealthy feed and grow fat on light.

There's no more need to waste the car's headlight.
We pass dull street lamps glowing mournfully,
Highlighting the cracks in the sidewalk and
The ugly homes squatting darkly behind.

The rain's stopped for now, leaving reflections,
Inky pools we drive through, leaving ripples.
The coffee left a bitter taste behind
I can't seem to get rid of, like ashes.

We pull up to a huge old hidden house
At the end of a long and empty road.
Dante checks the address, puts his hat on.
We step out and eye up what we can see.

There's a bunch of ancient cars sat outside
And places where windows have been built in
And bricked up: old relics of lighter times.
It's a sagging, depressing heap of stones.

I button my collar to hide the scar,
Ring the bell, full of dread, and clear my throat.
Dante's got each hand deep in a pocket,
Looking grim. He likes this place less than me.

A hook-nosed man in a suit opens up,
Ready to tell us to go and get lost,
But does a double take when he sees me.
It's bright behind him, house full of shining.

'You Mister North?' We pull out our badges.
He's not Mister North, but lets us come in,
Says he'll fetch the man. We remove our hats.
He leaves us to wait and admire the hall.

There are endless mirrors, amplifying
The huge chandelier, all twists of crystal.
Feels like I'm a stain on the carpet, like
I'm insulting the place with my presence.

Dante scowls at his reflection, glares down,
Doesn't like the sight of himself, head bowed.
I wonder if they're rich enough to have
A candle. Always wanted to see one.

North looks drunk, dark liquid swirling at hand.
He doesn't understand us, why we're here;
Doesn't look like he's ever seen a cop.
We follow him through to his main office.

'I'm real sorry, Mister North,' I tell him,
And it takes him a while to comprehend.
He offers us drinks, then money to leave,
As if the news will go along with us.

We sit quiet until he understands.
He doesn't shed a tear, just stares at us,
Drains his glass in gulps and keeps on staring,
Not quite sure how to react. What's proper.

We ask the questions that need to be asked
While he's calm, and get a lot of nothing.
North doesn't know if she was in danger.
It doesn't sound like they spoke much at all.

I ask to use the bathroom, and Dante
Gives me a look like I just shot the dog.
North doesn't seem to give a damn, points out,
Down the hall. His eyes are glazing over.

Bathroom's as big as my whole apartment.
I fumble a while, try to find the switch,
One arm clenched around my torso like I'm
Trying to stop my stomach from spilling.

It all comes out in a catastrophe.
One long stream of black and red debris.
I'm a heap of heaving bones clutching tight
To the bowl until I'm empty, hollow.

My ribs ache and my heart is a dull thud.
There are more mirrors here and I can't hide
From myself. I find a tap, splash water
On my face and drink until I can't breathe.

I take my time walking, recovering,
Passing white doors, more mirrors, more crystals,
Until I come across an open room,
Door flung wide. There's a woman on the bed.

She's sobbing into the sheets, staining them,
Mascara running in lines down her face.
I spend too long standing there. 'Mrs North?'
'Shit.' She notices me. 'Get the hell out!'

Dante's waiting for me by the front door
With the hook-nosed man. I can hear shouting
Somewhere else in the house. Some argument.
'We done?' I ask Dante. He scowls at me.

Back in the car, we escape the district.
Dante's relief is obvious. 'Ah, hell,'
He sighs, and he isn't sounding too mad.
One ordeal down and just one more to go.

'Dead end,' he tells me. 'The Norths know nothing.'
That's fine. Less leads and suspects to work through.
'There was one thing, though.' Dante looks thoughtful.
I trust his thoughts. 'Yeah?' 'Yeah. Notice the books?'

Now that he mentions it, there was something.
I can't place it. 'What about them, Dante?'
'Printed in ink,' he says. 'No normal books.
All printed words. The Norths can read off ink.'

We listen to the engine for a while,
Think about what that means. Maybe nothing.
Printed books are an ancient novelty
The wealthy like to indulge in sometimes.

I turn, grab the paper from the back seat,
Read it with my fingers, feel the words there
And try to imagine reading with eyes.
It strikes me as difficult and clumsy.

We pass a gate with no need for IDs.
They don't care who leaves, just who they let in.
Back to the comfortable dark of downtown.
My stomach still feels like it's full of knives.

> • <

Dante directs us beyond the blackness
Of downtown, past those places I frequent.
There's a sudden needling beneath my skin
Like yearning—as if my veins are hungry.

The withdrawals fade away for a while
And I emerge, clear, from inside myself
For the first time in hours. Feels good, like I'm
A drowning man who found a gasp of air.

We stop for gas before heading deeper
Uptown. Dante fills the car while I smoke.
There's some guy watching me across the way,
Frowning, lit by his headlight. I glare back.

He strides over before we can get gone,
This frowning short guy wearing spectacles.
Instinct makes me put my hand on my gun,
But he raises his hand, tells me his name.

'Wilson,' he says, 'I'm John Wilson. Big fan.'
I look for Dante, but he's gone to pay,
Left me trapped. I shake this John's hand and scowl
But he doesn't take the hint, keeps talking.

'Thought I recognised you. It was the scar.
Pretty messed-up case, but you sorted it.
Real nice to meet you, Mister Yorke. Real nice.
Hope you don't mind, but I'd love a picture.'

I stamp out my cigarette. 'I do mind.'
'Yeah,' he says, fumbles around. 'Sure, I guess.
But hey, listen. I'm a photographer.
Take my card, just in case.' He offers it.

'Come by. One for your kids, maybe.' He winks.
I don't correct him, just pocket the card,
And it's enough to make him leave, waving.
'Real nice to meet,' he calls. I grind my teeth.

Dante finally comes back, gets a look
That tells him he took too long. He grumbles,
Puts the car into gear and drives away.
I start to feel like I'm drowning again.

❯ • ❮

About the time we wind up getting close
To Vox's mind, her University,
A ringing starts in my ears like someone's
Finger's dragging round the top of a glass.

Dante says something I miss and parks up,
Leaving our car huddled up in the dark
With a dozen others. It's a bleak sight:
Empty black cars lined up like morgue corpses.

One catches my eye and I spend too long
Shining my torch through one of the windows.
It's an ancient model, long abandoned,
The keys still dangling from the ignition.

I have to cuff the back end of the torch
To stop it flickering. Damn thing's broken,
Erratic, never glows well. Got a crack
Across the lens the same shape as my scar.

They've got a sweet deal here: tuition fees
Set so high they can afford the best bulbs.
Nothing fancy, chandeliers or mirrors,
Just pure white bulbs scattered liberally.

The ringing in my ears starts to get sharp,
Heightens and reaches a painful climax.
I shake my head and it quietens down.
Dante calls over. 'Get a move on, Yorke.'

We pass another security gate,
Big men, bigger fists, looking serious.
They don't let any common trash through here,
Common trash like us without our badges.

Dante's mad, on the verge of violence,
Hates this place because he can't afford it
For his kids, doesn't make enough for them.
Doesn't make enough to give them a chance.

For once I'm the one helping calm him down,
Hand on a shoulder, muttering comfort.
I hate being here for my own reasons,
But I'm coming down way too hard to care.

We pass vast pillars, mirrors and portraits,
Stone floors polished to a reflective shine
And lights so bright I imagine that this
Is what it's like standing right next to stars.

We're greeted at reception by a girl.
She's elegant, sharply dressed, called Rachel.
For a moment I forget why we're here
Until Dante, irritable, starts up.

He asks for anyone we can talk to
About Vivian. Rachel smiles at him.
It's what I figure a sunrise is like:
A gentle emergence of brilliance.

We're escorted through to someone's office.
A short man, dressed well. One of her teachers:
Andrew Norton. And, he's a professor.
We all shake hands out of formality.

I look him up and down. Pointed grey beard
And face lined like a map of the city.
I turn and thank Rachel as she leaves us,
Watch her shoes click across the shining floor.

Words travel between Dante and Norton
But I'm not listening, I'm too distracted.
The room's filled with things I don't recognise,
Strange-looking bits of old machinery.

I get up and look around while they talk,
Glancing over rusted metal objects,
Rows of half-broken books covered in dust,
Heaped-up papers, diagrams and designs.

Sat on one shelf is something out of place.
It's a hand-carved wooden idol of Phos;
Face of a star, arms spread in welcoming.
Didn't think he was a religious man.

    It strikes me enough that I interrupt.
'Hey, professor, why have you got this here?'
I lift Phos up from the shelf carefully,
A victim of my dad's faith, even here.

    Dante halts mid-sentence, lowers his pen.
Norton smiles like I asked the right question.
'Just as a reminder, Inspector Yorke.'
And he leaves it there, makes me ask, 'Of what?'

    'There are people, waifs, "ghosts", in this city
Who believe that we have always been here
In the dark. It's far too easy for me
To forget quite how few know what I know.'

    I look at the idol, our star-faced god.
'Tell me, inspector. What do you believe?'
Good question. I don't know what I believe.
I'm not superstitious. 'In hell, I guess.'

    Norton gets up, rummages through a drawer.
Dante has his head bowed like he's in prayer,
But I know he's counting down in his head:
Exercises his therapist gave him.

    'Do you know from where Vox gets its power?'
Norton finds what he was searching round for.
'Sure. The Hearts: Aquila, Corvus, Cancer.'
'But have you ever seen one up close?' 'No.'

It looks like it might be made of crystal,
Or that it might be some kind of machine..
'Well, neither have I. This is all I have.
One to one hundred scale. This is a Heart.'

I forget Phos and approach the model.
Try, somehow, to understand it, its shape.
'Doesn't look like anything,' I tell him,
But he's looking at Phos, admiring Him.

'That statue is my constant reminder
That while I may know our great histories,
The common man does not. He only knows
The dark in which he was born. Your hell, Yorke.'

The professor is too much. 'Yeah. My hell.'
The ringing in my ears returns in force.
Dante raises his head and glares at me.
'So, about Vivian,' he tries again.

I shake my head some more, but the ringing
Isn't going anywhere: here to stay.
Can't get those words out of my head, either:
Your hell, Yorke. Your hell I stare at the Heart.

'Vivian,' says the professor, thoughtful.
'Bright girl. Hard working. Sad to hear she's gone.'
He seems sincere enough, but not surprised,
Like he knew about her before we showed.

'Any rivals?' asks Dante, forging on.
'None come to mind.' Then, Dante quickly drops:
'Can you think of a reason someone might
Leave her with her veins full of liquid light?'

And this seems to surprise the professor
More than the news of Vivian's murder.
'Pardon?' He frowns, mumbles. 'The use of drugs
Is strictly not permitted on campus.'

Me and Dante exchange a glance. He knows
Something's struck home with the good professor.
'Looks like someone filled her veins up with light.
Maybe not Prometheus. Much brighter.'

Both of us try to gauge his reaction.
He looks like he's too warm, starting to sweat.
'The conversion alone would...' he mutters.
Then, louder, 'That's simply not possible.'

'What's not possible?' I ask, lean forwards.
'Well, from what little I do understand,
Prometheus is very volatile
At high rates of dilution, let alone...'

'Look. The drug at that concentration burns
Through flesh. Maybe even through muscle, bone.'
Dante shakes his head, taps his pen sharply.
'We have a body that says otherwise.'

The professor looks trapped, takes way too long
To come up with a reply. 'I don't see—'
'Professor,' says Dante, like he's closing
In on prey, 'what, exactly, don't you see?'

We wait while he regains his composure.
'I am happy to help you gentlemen,
Any way I can. However, right now,
I have matters to attend to.' He stands.

It's too late for him. Dante's on his case,
Knows that something's up, something's rattled him.
Dante stays right where he is, keeps going.
'This is a very important matter.'

'Certainly…' The professor hesitates.
There's a pause and I use it to think fast.
I stand as well, put my hat on, gesture
And turn to depart. 'Dante. We're done here.'

We join a stream of students in the hall.
Dante looks at me like I wrecked the case.
I can hear him follow, can feel his rage,
His eyes burning through the back of my skull.

'What in the name of Phos was that, Virgil?'
He hisses. 'You know we fucking had him!'
'We had something,' I say. 'But not enough.'
'Oh, come on. You saw him. He knew something.'

I stop, make sure nobody's listening in.
'Trust me,' I tell him. 'You know me. Trust me.'
'Trust you?' Dante spits, stains the stone below.
'You're a fucking junkie, Virgil. You're fucked.'

I grit my teeth, take the insult because
It's no lie. 'Sure, but you've got to trust me.
I've got a better plan.' Students trail past.
'He was never gonna tell us enough.'

'Shit.' Dante sighs, searches round for a smoke.
It's as good as I'm gonna get from him.
We make our way out, past the reception.
Rachel smiles at me as we pass her by.

Someone's keyed the squad car. Dante kicks it,
Curses, lets out some of his frustration.
We drive in silence the rest of the way,
Joined in mutual hate for our city.

>•<

An hour on and I'm at the city quay,
Standing at the edge of an empty pier,
Fresh bottle of whisky at hand, untouched,
Eyes closed, listening to the waves wash below.

I don't bother signing off any more.
Don't care what they pay me or if they do.
Never enough for Dante's family,
Always enough for my fucking hobbies.

I shine my torch down on the black water
Until its batteries die, fleeting light
Revealing nothing, reflecting nothing.
Don't know what I'm looking for, anyway.

Feeling around in the dark with my hands,
I find the edge and swing my tired legs out
Over the ocean, think about its size,
How big it's meant to be, how small I am.

I can hear it rushing around the pier,
Our dark planet's unpredictable tides
Eroding the edges of our city,
Slowly turning Vox back into debris.

I know how this cycle's going to end.
I do this once every week: sit here, tired,
At the end of my tether, feeling like
I might just pitch over into the black.

Here comes my big ultimatum again.
Either I walk away now and get clean
Or let myself fall, swallowed by the black.
This is my fleeting weekly victory.

Each attempt, I get up, take a shower,
Head to an uptown bar, smile, drink, until
The craving gets too bad and wind up right
Back where I belong, veins full of glowing.

I don't know why I keep telling my lie:
That I can fix the mess I made of me.
Truth is, I'm broken like the rest of Vox.
Most common cause of death is suicide.

In school they try to teach you how to cope
With the constant dark, tell you to find light
And avoid being immersed in blackness.
They fairly know what it does to a man.

The city's not what made me this way, though.
After the 'hanging', my case, my big break,
A dark took up residence in my head:
Some unmovable piece of nothingness.

I guess I figured it was physical,
That I could fill it up with liquid light,
Fill myself up like poor dead Vivian.
Turns out I was right. An hour a cycle.

Before I know it, the bottle's half gone.
In a surge of violence, I smash it,
Send the stem spinning into the ocean,
Wonder what the fuck I'm doing back here.

I've got a job I need to do. My plan.
I cut myself deep as I try to stand,
Pulling shards out of the skin of my hands,
Watching my dull-glowing blood crawl down me.

For a moment I'm at the edge again,
One step away from my oblivion,
But I walk away as always, this time
Needing something to bind my weeping hands.

I take the long route to my apartment
To throw off the whisky's worst, sober up.
I take a cold shower, find my good coat
And head out to an uptown bar. Hopeful.

I've played this moment out so many times,
The same performance over and over,
But this might just be my time. I'm allowed
My brief reprieve, my hours caught up in hope.

> • <

I head to a blues bar I remember,
Hoping I'm right, hoping to get lucky.
It's one of the places I like round here,
All lit up in blue for the atmosphere.

Barman knows his way around whisky, too,
Gets the temperature right, saves the flavour.
Not that it matters too much in the end.
Ten down, it all tastes the same anyway.

Doorman eyes me up, lets me slide inside
Because he knows me, my reputation.
Round here I'm a kind of celebrity,
Even if I look halfway to the grave.

I enter and there she is at the bar,
Radiant as a spark against the blue.
I cough, clear my throat, check my reflection
And head over, trying for dignity.

Rachel gives me one of her polite smiles.
Looks like she's halfway through a tall cocktail.
She doesn't make a move to head away,
Which I choose to take as a compliment.

'Inspector,' she says. 'A sight for sore eyes.'
I remove my hat, order a whisky,
Ask what she's drinking, but she shakes her head,
Taps the cocktail, tells me she's good for now.

'Call me Virgil,' I say, taking my time
With the whisky, sipping at it slowly.
There's some music and it's not unpleasant,
Just background noise, something smooth, relaxing.

She looks almost as tired as I'm feeling,
Holding on to her drink like she's fallen
Into the ocean and it's a lifebelt.
But hell, she looks full of life, full of youth.

I realise I've been staring at her
And so does she, smile turning embarrassed.
'So,' she says, 'what's a guy like you doing
All the way over in a place like this?'
    Funny. I guess I consider this bar
A classy place, bright and respectable,
While to her it's a place to hide away.
Somewhere to drink alone, escape the world.
    'Where's your friend?' she asks, looking for Dante.
'Home,' I tell her. 'He's got some kids to watch.'
She finishes her drink, asks about me.
'You got anybody at home, Virgil?'
    'No family,' I tell her. 'Just whisky.'
It's meant to be a joke, but it comes out
Depressing, like there's truth in it, and hell,
Maybe there is. I've got nobody else.
    She laughs anyway, makes me crack a smile,
And it feels unfamiliar, a piece
Of the old Yorke making an appearance.
I place my empty glass down on the bar.
    We talk a bit, but she works me out, says,
'So you're here to ask me about Norton?'
I frown, don't reply, let her weigh me up.
'Buy me a drink,' she tells me, taps the bar.
    Looks like the drinks are on me, and that's fine.
After a while, she's got me trying drinks
I'd never go near: colourful cocktails
That taste like fruit and strong, strong alcohol.

I lose track of what we're talking about,
Find a calm, cloudy numbness in my head
And stay there, somewhere on the edge of content.
I get caught up in the drinks, in her eyes.

Even when I start shaking, getting bad
Cravings, realise I haven't eaten,
Realise I want, need, Prometheus,
I stay, getting worse but still in control.

Only when the lights go out and stay out
Do I remember myself, who I am.
I come crashing back to reality,
Suddenly aware of what's going on.

The situation is a sucker punch,
Forcing me out of my seat at the bar,
Hearing the whimpers of the lost and scared
Suddenly plunged into complete darkness.

Something is very wrong here. Critical.
The power's never gone out, not in Vox.
Through the cloudy numbness of alcohol
I can feel Rachel's hand reaching for mine.

'Shit,' I tell her. 'I need to deal with this.'
The barman is appealing for order,
Checking the fuses again, the lightbulbs,
But he can't find anything wrong with them.

I get a shock when something meets my face,
But it's Rachel pressing her lips to me,
Telling me to go, like I'm some hero
That can fix the dark, banish it away.

Outside, the situation is bad, worse.
Looks like the whole block is out. I can hear
Wailing, screaming, people running past me.
A thousand noises heralding chaos.

I find my way down the street, on through crowds,
Warm, breathing bodies not sure what to do,
Milling about in big herds like cattle,
People made stupid by the lack of light.

Nobody can find a glow, power's out.
Torches are stolen, smothered and broken,
Ruined in sudden outbursts of panic.
The loudest are praying wildly to Phos.

I find a phone box, but it's surrounded,
So I fire my revolver in the air,
Use noisy words, 'Police! Get out the way!'
And make myself a path through to a call.

'This is Yorke. What the fuck is happening?'
Head office sounds just as bad as out here,
Loud voices, phones ringing. They put me through
To a higher-up and I don't know why.

'This Yorke?' It's a voice I don't recognise.
'This is Yorke.' I have to shout to be heard.
'Shit, son. Been trying to get hold of you.'
'What's happening? Why's the power gone out?'

'I'm sending a car to get you, okay?'
I tell him where I am and try again,
'Look. You've got to tell me what's happening.'
'Sit tight, son. We're bringing you in for this.'

He hangs up and I slam the receiver,
Nearly breaking the damn phone as I do.
I step outside, caught up in the chaos,
Unable to think clearly, still too drunk.
   Shit. I shake my head, try to clear my thoughts,
But all I can think about is Rachel
All I can think about is Vivian.
All I can think about is my next fix.

> • <

I'm in the back of a heavy squad van.
It's too dark outside. Our escorts are bright,
Clearing us a path through the endless crowds,
Flashing red, revealing frightened faces.
   There's a tall man sitting opposite me
I think I should recognise, but can't place.
He's smoking a cigar, gold tooth glinting,
The edge of his grey moustache stained yellow.
   We listen to the sounds of the city
Going to hell. Sounds like a reckoning,
Like people having their last hope taken,
Cursing up at the sky: our absent star.
   There's more rumbling and we're free of the dark
And the crowds, surrounded by silhouettes.
Here's a district that still has some power,
Filling up with wandering refugees.

I run a hand down my face, try to think,
Try to hide my hunger and sober up.
I recognise him now, my companion.
He's the chief, Chester Garfield, my boss.

    'You up to this, son? It's gonna be tough.'
His suit is well cut, tailored, expensive.
I still don't get it, what's happening here.
'Up to what, sir?' At least he's talking now.

    'He asked for you by name. "Inspector Yorke,"
He told me. "Bring him. He can get it back.",
He leans in towards me, reeking of smoke.
'Reckon you can find it? Be honest now.'

    Feels like I'm missing something important.
Might be the alcohol making me dumb.
I can't join the dots. It's real frustrating
And I'm all out of patience. 'Find what, sir?'

    The chief leans back, is hidden in shadow.
He tells me, but makes it sound trivial.
'There's been a break-in at a Heart vault, son.
Someone's gone and killed a lot of people.'

    It takes me time to process properly.
Outside, we pass through a reinforced gate
Of the kind meant to keep everyone out,
Not divide the hungry from the wealthy.

    'But I've got a case, sir. Vivian North.'
He tilts his head to one side, observes me.
'You're off the North case. This is your case now.'
Our van stops. 'Come on now, son. He's waiting.'

> • <

I am like a cowering animal,
Trying to escape from the wide white eyes
Watching me pass by, some alive, some dead,
All staring at the scar around my throat.

My head's a tangled-up mess of cravings
Getting worse, telling me to run away,
Get out from this light place filled with corpses.
I want, *need*, food and sleep and liquid light.

There's flashing cameras and people moving,
Loud voices and lengthy shifting shadows.
I'm being led down a long corridor
Made red by coloured bulbs or maybe blood.

Garfield is telling me things as we go,
But his voice sounds like it's under water;
It's booming and muffled at the same time.
All I do is nod and follow behind.

There's a huge room at the end like a hall
And it's the brightest place I've ever been,
The widest space I've ever seen at once,
Like we're stood at the centre of a star.

For a moment it feels like I've gone blind,
My eyes so overwhelmed there's nothing else,
Until, like a disembodied shadow,
A silhouette approaches through the light.

If I squint, I can just about see him.
He offers a hand covered in dark skin
To me, maybe as a sort of greeting,
But I don't react in kind, take that hand.

'Inspector,' he says. 'About time you came.'
My eyes start to adjust so I can see
What this room is. Looks like this is the vault:
Thick stone walls, only one way in or out.

Right now, there's a crooked scar through a wall;
A great rent leaking the warmth of the place,
Surrounded by tumbled-down blocks of stone
And dozens of dead people thrown like dolls.

The hardest part to look at in the room
Is the centre, where there's a mass of pipes
Arranged like the frayed ends of bits of string
Around a vacant cradle made of glass.

'I've never been left in the dark before,'
The man is saying to me. 'Before now.'
'They tore out my Heart.' He's angry, snarling.
'They stole it from me. My Heart. My damn Heart.'

I can see him better now, and he's mad,
Face clenched up tight, knotted, gnarled in fury.
I don't understand how his skin is dark,
Like it's been badly burned or painted black.

'Yorke,' says the chief, 'this is Mister Cancer.'
They're both staring at me, appraising me,
Waiting to see how I'm going to deal
With this catastrophe. Like I know how.

This is so far beyond me. I don't know
What I should be doing or where to start.
All I know is what my body's saying,
And right now it's saying I need to run.

I look them both in the eye and wonder
How they can't see I'm falling apart here.
Don't they know I'm as much a disaster
As that hole torn clean through the wall back there?

'I need to sleep,' I say, and my words slur.
Cancer's expression shifts. He looks unsure,
Glances at the chief for affirmation
That I'm better at my job than I look.

Even though I'm standing dead on my feet,
Garfield's reaction seems way off to me.
He smiles, says, 'Virgil's had a long cycle,
Ain't that right, son?' His hand grips my shoulder.

'Sure,' I say, 'cause it's what he wants to hear,
And I move away, retreat from the light,
Shiver into the dark among the dead,
Back where I belong, away from this place.

'Yorke,' calls Cancer. 'You need to find my Heart.'
I stop, the twitching wreckage of a man,
Shout back over my shoulder, 'Call Dante.
He can take care of this for now. He's good.'

I somehow find my way out of the vault
And back into the dark of the city.
My head's a frenzied mess of addiction,
Forcing me on despite my need for sleep.

My skin feels like it's crawling round my flesh
And every breath I take feels like my last,
Like I'm back on that chair, noose round my neck,
Gasping and gasping, mouth wide and desperate.

There's a guy I know up this end of town.
He's expensive, but makes sales on demand.
I don't remember the walk to his door,
Just my face against the rough wood of it.

I give him every cent I have on me.
Even my cigarettes, still damp from rain.
Hell, I try to sell him my coat, my hat,
But the rest is enough for one small phial.

It glows between my shuddering fingers
And I don't make it to my apartment;
Huddled up in some forgotten corner
Of the city, piled high with trash and me.

Difficult to find a vein in the dark,
But I can be persistent when needed,
And I've had practice. So much damn practice.
The needle feels at home puncturing me.

I inhale sharply, hear my booming heart,
Imagine it's Vox's bright Hearts pumping
Light across the city and within me,
Bringing with it a rushing ecstasy.

I forget that my name is Virgil Yorke.
I forget that I am not a city,
That I am not Vox. I become the streets,
The sky and everything else in between.

> • <

He doesn't look like anything special.
Your average Joe: smart round spectacles,
Neat suit, balding. Middle-management type.
He doesn't say much, either. Hums a tune.
   I let it happen. Let him string me up.
The pistol he has only punctuates
The unsaid. We both know what's happening.
Another cycle, another hanging.

SECOND CYCLE

Don't know what time it is when I get home,
But the phone's ringing and keeps on ringing.
I let it go, find something edible
And feel the ache in my bones as I sit.

It feels like I've been chewed up and spat out,
But the booze is out of my system now,
The Prometheus a warm afterglow,
And my head's together enough to think.

I'm in a hell of a bad position.
I should be out there now, finding the Heart,
But it's too big a mess. I'm overwhelmed.
I can't get Vivian out of my head.

The phone starts ringing for the seventh time,
So I pick up, just to see who it is.
Of course it's Dante. 'Shit, Yorke, about time
You woke up. I'm coming over, okay?'

I mutter, 'sure,' hang up, make my own call.
The operator directs me on through
The DEA, and from them I find Fife.
He sounds surprised to be hearing from me.

    'Yorke? Shouldn't you be looking for the Heart?'
'Look. What about the North case. You on it?'
There's a pause. 'No,' he says. 'Not any more.
Your department now. Did nobody say?'

    I rub my temple, try to stop the pain
Spreading through my head before it gets far.
I fumble around for some batteries,
Gotta be a few left over in here.

    'Nobody's saying anything,' I say.
'Yeah, nobody ever does,' he tells me.
'Look, Yorke. You need anything, let me know.
Can't have sons of bitches stealing our Hearts.'

    'Sure.' He hangs up and the phone rings again.
I let it go, keep on searching around
Until I find a pair of batteries
And my torch, hefting the heavy metal.

    I slot the fresh set of batteries in,
Cuff it until it emits a weak glow,
Note I still need to get the damn thing fixed
And take a quick glance round my apartment.

    The place is way worse than I imagined.
Looks like a squat or some kind of drug den.
No time to clean up. I sigh, grab my coat,
Head on downstairs to meet Dante outside.

He's leant against a wall, smoking, looks wrecked,
Like he hasn't slept. Maybe he hasn't.
'Shit, Yorke. We're pretty damn fucked,' he tells me.
I don't disagree. He hands me a smoke.

We stay in silence for a little while,
Listen to the sounds of the city's streets.
No end of loud voices, engines, sirens,
But no more panic. Sounds like it's died down.

'They're diverting power from the others,'
Says Dante, like he knows what I'm thinking.
'One city, three Hearts. We're fucking lucky.
Anywhere else, we'd be completely screwed.'

Dante's eyes are bloodshot, lids drooping low,
Looks like he's running on coffee alone.
'And you're all across the papers again.
Congrats.' He spits. 'You fucking idiot.'

'Not my choice,' I tell him, sucking smoke deep.
'Yeah?' Dante doesn't believe me. 'But why?
Why in hell's name would they put you on this?
Everyone knows you're washed-up. It's not news.'

'Hell if I know,' I mumble. 'But look, thanks.'
'For what?' 'For covering for me.' He nods,
Stamps out his cigarette, rolls up his sleeves.
'Sure, Yorke. So, you want the good news or what?'

'Good news?' By his tone, I'm guessing it's not.
'We're fucked because whoever took the Heart
Knew what he was doing. It's a clean job.
Real professional. Left nothing behind.'

'Shit. So what, then? Do we have anything?'
'Not a fucking thing. Twenty-five dead guards,
An empty cradle and a wall that looks
Like someone ran a fucking train through it.'

He's brought his own car, left the headlight on
So we can see the street and passing cars.
It's only weak; shivering fragile light
Just bright enough so we can see ourselves.

If we stay here too long, ghosts will show up:
Wasted folk made ghouls by light starvation,
Drawn to the headlight by desperation.
They get violent real easy round here.

'So where do you wanna start?' Dante asks.
'I don't.' 'Shit, Yorke, be serious for once.'
'I am. We've gotta do something else first.
Need to find out who's on the North case now.'

'Come on, Yorke—' he starts, but I interrupt.
'Hell, I know how important the Heart is,
But we've got some information to share.
The professor knew something, remember?'

For once, Dante shrugs, agrees with me, 'Sure.'
'So let's head to HQ, pass that along,
And then get on the Heart. Is that all right?'
He shrugs, squints at me. 'You look like shit, Yorke.'

'So do you.' We get in the car, start up
And pull out just as the first ghost turns up.
She looks hungry, thin, spindly arms held out,
Covered in sores. We leave her in darkness.

〉 • 〈

Might be the last of the Prometheus,
But I feel good for once. I have control.
Enough clear space in my head to think straight.
Dante's right: I'm washed up. Something here's wrong.

Why the fuck am I on this case at all?
This question feels important, feels weighty.
Those early hours at Cancer's vault were wrong;
The chief shouldn't have been letting me go.

So what, then? I try to think more, think deep,
But Dante turns a corner hard, swerves round,
Yells, swears at the ghosts in his way out there,
Blocking the road, gathered round some machine.

Remnants of the blackout are everywhere
And nobody's out clearing up the roads.
Nobody cares enough now it's over;
Back to staring at bulbs behind closed doors.

There's a crunch and hiss from the car's engine,
Smoke billowing up, out from the front grill.
The car rattles, shudders like it's dying,
Stuttering and failing along the street.

'Shit,' growls Dante. He stops the car, exits,
Inspects the engine and curses some more.
'Second fucking time this month. Piece of shit.'
He kicks it. 'We're walking the last blocks, Yorke.'

I watch out while he unscrews the headlight
To keep it away from the hands of ghosts.
We've broken down in the wrong neighbourhood;
Rent's low here because there's no easy glows.

I keep one hand on my gun as we go,
Striding through the dark because if we light
A torch here we'll get stabbed or shot for it.
We tread down cracked roads, crunch through broken glass.

I don't know why I keep my eyes open.
Some human instinct in the dark maybe;
Eyes wide, ready to catch any small glint,
Any sign there's something beyond the black.

We pass laboured breathing, stinking bodies,
Other cops shouting, hailing, greeting us,
Some lost folk, people running, walking slow,
And the silent, present only in warmth.

Dante doesn't give a damn, powers on,
Announces himself with his heavy feet.
I'm subtler, like to go quiet, evade,
Avoid others. Much less trouble that way.

Two blocks on, past what sounds like some road works,
A dark café filled with unseen diners
And an invisible fight between friends,
We come to one of the precinct's back gates.

There's a man on duty who tips his cap,
Lets us through. He's lit by the small green glint
Of light leaking up out through the keyhole,
And even that seems bright after our walk.

The office is a mess of yelling cops,
Shouting at each other about cases,
Paperwork, guns, the city, the darkness,
The everycycle chaos of our work.

We head to our department, Homicide,
Well aware of being watched as we go.
These guys know who I am, recognise me
As the cop who solved the case they couldn't.

Our own office is no less of a mess;
Colleagues and superiors shouting out,
Trying to be heard over ringing phones,
Thumping boots, humming fans and each other.

I find Santiago behind his desk,
Feet up, smoking a cigarette, eyes high,
Watching his ceiling fan turn overhead.
'Virgil,' he says, without looking away.

I knock on his desk. 'Who's on the North case?'
'What?' 'You heard me. Who's got the North case now?'
He looks at me at last. 'You look like shit.'
'Santiago, I don't have time for this.'

'Sure.' He swings his feet round and shuts his eyes.
'Look. Last I heard, DEA have it now.'
When he opens his eyes, he's serious.
'Not that it matters.' 'But—' 'But nothing, Yorke.'

Dante steps up. The two of them are friends
Of a sort. They have an understanding.
'We've got some leads that need passing along,'
He says. 'Important leads, Santiago.'

Our colleague shuffles through some paperwork.
'I don't know. I've got nothing. But look, guys,
There's a man turned up, been asking for you.
Came from the University hours back.'

My breathing stops short. 'Professor Norton?'
But Santiago shakes his head. 'Sorry.
Some doctor, I think. Didn't take his name,
But he's pretty jumpy. You should see him.'

I exchange a glance with Dante, who shrugs.
Santiago gestures to the back rooms.
'He's in one of the interview holdings.
Someone's with him I think, got him calmed down.'

'Santiago?' I say, loud to be heard.
He's picked up the phone, but covers it, says,
'What?' 'The North case. Find out who has it, right?'
'Sure,' he waves me away. 'Sure. Whatever.'

We find the doctor waiting as promised,
Sitting nervous in an interview chair,
Hands wound tight around a now-empty mug.
I shut the door and the room gets quiet.

'Detective Inspector Yorke!' He stands up,
Reaches out a trembling and sweaty hand,
Shakes mine and then Dante's in a hurry,
Like he's got some place important to be.

'I-I tried calling but I couldn't get—
Nobody could get through to you, no time—
So I came down and— I'm very sorry
To trouble you like this, but I'm not sure—'

'Slow down,' says Dante. 'Sit down. Calm down, sir.'
'Of-of course.' He does as he's told. 'But I'm—'
'What's your name?' I find a chair opposite.
'Doctor Magnusson, sir. I work at the—'

'You work at the Uni'. Sure. We've been told.'
He's a small guy, hunched up tight in his seat,
Blinking fast behind his round spectacles
And trembling constantly. He looks damn scared.

'So, how can we help you, doc'?' asks Dante.
'Look, I…' He takes a deep breath, tries again.
'You must find Cancer immediately.
The Heart. I don't think you quite understand.'

'What is it we don't understand, doctor?'
'Well, ah, I am one of the few people
In this city who has studied the Hearts.
I know what they are and what they can do.'

'All right. So what's with all the urgency?'
'I-I am quite worried that, ah, Cancer
May have been taken by persons who don't
Know what a Heart is and what it can do.'

Dante's got his notepad out, pen scribbling,
Taking notes. There's something about the doc'
That's contagious. It might be his panic.
I can feel my heart start beating faster.

'How do you mean?' Dante asks, carefully.
Magnusson removes his glasses, shaking,
Trying to wipe his sweat from the lenses.
'Listen,' he says, grimly. 'The Hearts are stars.'

Dante stops writing. He looks up. 'Huh? What?'
'The Hearts are stars. They are, ah, compacted.
Contained, you might say, at the moment of,
Ah, supernova. They are... *raw...* power.'

I can't contain the concept in my head.
It's too big. Don't know why I never thought
About what the Hearts were made of before.
Always just assumed something bright, I guess.

'You're saying,' says Dante, 'the Hearts are stars?'
He seems as lost as I am, maybe more.
'Yes, well, yes. But. Okay, yes, they are stars,
And you need to understand. Please listen.

'The Hearts are nearly impenetrable.
The containment used is, ah, beautiful.
Technology I barely understand,
Far before our time, you see. Before us.'

I close my eyes, run a hand down my face,
Try to un-hear the bad word he just said,
But it's too late. I lower my head down.
'Doc',' I say, hoarse. 'What do you mean, "nearly"?'

'Ah, yes. That's what I mean, Inspector Yorke.
There is quite a slim possibility
That a particularly determined
Team might be able to breach the, the, ah—'

Dante's voice is a growl. He's stopped writing.
'Right. So, a breach. And then what would happen?'
A lengthy quiet takes over the room
As Magnusson comes up with a reply.

'Annihilation,' he says, quietly.
My hands are shaking. Might be withdrawals,
Might be the hangover. I hope it is.
I press them against the rough wood table.

'Of what?' asks Dante. 'A block? The city?'
The doc's voice is nearly a whisper now.
'The physics are... ah... astronomical.
I-I really can't even fathom how—'

I stand, lean forwards over the table.
'The whole city?' I ask, looking him straight.
He shakes his head slowly, sadly, trembling.
'Inspector Yorke... much more than the city.

'A-a breach would necessarily mean
The breach of all the other Hearts we have.
The combined release of energy would...
No-one, Inspector Yorke, could even dream...'

He begins to mumble. I get closer.
The weak bulb hanging above flickers once.
'We wouldn't... we wouldn't live to see it.
We would be turned to dust, or less than dust.

'A breach would... would... unleash a violence
Like nothing else. It would be an event
Leaving no Vox, no dark star and no... *us*.
Nothing to mark that we were ever here.'

❯ • ❮

Dante puts a team together to help
Because neither of us know what to do.
I remain disconnected and absent,
Like I'm an observer, not taking part.
    I sit by and watch cops, men, swarm like rats,
Fighting for space, fighting for attention,
Crying out to one another, screeching,
Unable to reach a kind of order.
    Even as I'm summoned to see the press,
They're still arguing, with no progress made.
Dante sits at the centre of it all,
Cradling his head as if it's too heavy.

> • <

I'm led through to a dull conference hall
Where reporters are sat in rank and file,
Seniors up front, freshmen at the back,
All hands raised high like they're praying to Phos.
    There are some fans, but the heat is still bad.
Too many bodies crammed in together.
I remove my hat, wipe sweat from my brow
And find my place on stage, front and centre.
    There's a collection of hot white spotlights
Aimed at the stage, at my face, at my scar,
Revealing every blemish, every flaw,
And keeping me pinned like I'm under fire.

Their faces are dark. It's a sea of hands.
Some of those hands are waving up at me,
Others clicking, vying for attention.
A few are still, holding tape recorders.

There's a sudden flash, a puff of grey smoke
And a man shouting that I need to pose.
I'm startled, trying to clear my vision.
I hate all this: the cameras and the press.

I find some place inside myself to hide,
Leave my tongue running on automatic
And give them all the regular answers:
Vague, non-committal and reassuring.

We're gonna find the Heart. Of course we are.
We've got a bunch of leads we're working on.
It'll be back by the end of the week,
We're sure. Don't worry yourselves, we're on it.

At some point during the press conference,
I remove my coat and find the badge there:
A solid imitation-gold crescent.
I place it on the table before me.

Don't know why it has my attention now,
But it does. I'm wondering why I'm here,
Why I'm still doing this damn job at all,
And that badge is the best answer I have.

It's cheap, easy to make, easy to forge,
And they're dime-a-dozen down some precincts,
But I used to have lots of pride in mine.
It meant something to me, some long time back.

Hell, there's still something there now, as I stare,
Admiring the cracked edges, and the dents.
It's a badge hard won and harder to keep.
Guess I'm a man of the law after all.

Some reporter's been asking me something
While I've been lost in thoughts about my badge
And repeats himself again, sounds annoyed,
Shouts, 'Why would someone steal one of the Hearts?'

I pick my badge up and squeeze it tightly,
Until it hurts and I might be bleeding,
And I don't tell him that the Heart's a bomb.
I don't tell him anything true at all.

'We're looking at a number of motives,'
I tell him, tell them all, tell the city.
'Nothing we're able to disclose right now.
But you can rest easy. We're on the case.'

He's persistent, our man among many,
Keeps trying. 'But why would someone want it?'
And they all seem interested, keep quiet,
Wait for my reply, all hands still raised high.

I stand up. 'We've answered enough for now.
Thanks for your questions.' I put my hat on,
Turn away, hear the crowd's dismay rising,
Demanding more of me than I can give.

Their calling voices rise to a climax,
Become a wordless rush of noise instead:
The city's collective accusation
Of dissatisfaction, howling for more.

Outside, I finally open my hand,
Already bound once and bleeding again
In the shape of a crescent, red on white.
I put my badge away in a pocket.

> • <

My father taught me a few things in life.
Never shave against the grain, never smoke,
Have pride in what you do no matter what,
And above all else, don't die by yourself.

He was the kindest guy I ever knew.
Raised me by himself, put his entire life
Into his business: a haberdasher
Making the best damn hats you ever saw.

I know all there is to know about hats
From him. He used to make them without light,
Putting them together by touch alone;
The skin of his fingers too thick to prick.

It was never profitable enough
To send me off to University,
Which damn near broke him down. Too proud a man.
He passed on the same week I joined the force.

I was away on some rookie mission
When I should have been sat at his bedside.
He died alone, and I remain ashamed
Of myself. One more shadow haunting me.

My dad taught me a lot of things in life.
If you meet a girl worth saving, save her,
Make her remember you. Make her your own.
And above all else, don't die by yourself.

> • <

I take a break, escape from the office
And find myself heading down flights of stairs
Into the cold, the air-con hissing ice
At me as I pass, pulling my coat close.
    They're busy getting nowhere fast upstairs,
Running in circles, running into walls,
Too many cops making bad suggestions
And no real progress. They're all lost up there.
    I pass broken bulbs nobody's replaced
And others close to dying. Dark patches
And short flickering havens in between.
In places I have to switch my torch on.
    It's only when I get to the basement
I realise why I'm down here at all.
This is the morgue, where our victims are shelved,
Cut open and taken apart for clues.
    At least they have something of a budget
Here. Enough for some stable bars of light
Humming bare and pale in the constant chill,
Somehow making the place feel much colder.

I attempt to ignite a cigarette,
But no repeat scratching makes a match work.
I'm left shivering, breath steaming, dead smoke
Dangling sadly from the edge of my mouth.

I feel nervous, like I'm out on a date,
About to meet a girl, set eyes on her.
In a way I am, except this girl's dead.
I'm down here to find Vivian's body.

One of the attendants tries to help me,
But doesn't understand my descriptions.
He looks through his files, but can't find her name,
Can't find any girl filled up with glowing.

He's got no memory of her coming,
Of shelving her, of hearing about her.
But he's a helpful guy, sympathetic,
Keeps on looking anyway, just in case.

We go in deeper, walls made of metal
And patterned by dozens of square steel doors,
Pulling on shelves and reading through toe-tags,
Looking for a mistake that's just not there.

'This is the only place she could have come,'
I tell him, and he agrees, searching notes.
He can't find any record of a call
Asking for someone to come pick her up.

After a while, he stops, shrugs his shoulders,
Asks me if I'm sure. Truth be told, I'm not.
I'm beginning to question myself now.
It's looking like Vivian's disappeared.

I try to strike some more matches and think,
But it's real hard. My head's a complete mess.
I start to wonder if I made her up;
If Vivian North even existed.

The case seemed crazy enough. Glowing girl
Found dead down a dead-end back alleyway,
Bright enough to leave a mark in my mind.
Maybe she was a figment of my dreams.

Prometheus makes you hallucinate,
Makes you feel such intense euphoria
And paranoia, wholeness and madness.
Maybe Vivian was another trip.

Just as it feels like I'm losing myself
To total self-doubt, I strike one more match
And feel the heat of the flame as it works,
Igniting my damn cigarette at last.

I lean against a cold wall and inhale,
Hold, letting the cigarette do its work.
Another drug to keep me going straight.
Another drug to balance them all out.

Of course I didn't imagine the girl.
The reason I can't seem to forget her
Is because of how real she was to me:
A piece of brightness in my dark city.

I remain surrounded by the deceased,
Neatly shelved away in rows, as I smoke.
Feels like I'm another dead man down here,
Just one cycle from being shelved myself.

〉 • 〈

'Grab your hat, Yorke. We've got a lead. Let's go.'
Dante pushes the door ajar and waits.
I find my hat beside a filled ashtray,
Grab it and follow him to reception.

'What kind of lead?' I ask, as he signs forms,
Secures us another squad car to use.
We're led through to a sparsely lit compound
Filled with rows of shining, proud vehicles.

Dante's gracious and waits while I throw up,
Empty what little there is inside me,
Keep heaving until I'm hollow again.
The ache that goes down to my bones is back.

I stumble into the passenger seat
As Dante starts up, puts our car in gear,
Drives up a ramp and into the city.
It feels good to get out of the office.

'Friend of mine,' says Dante, 'gave me a call.'
He doesn't elaborate, instead says,
'Mostly just wanted to get out of there.
Nobody's getting a fucking thing done.'

I wind the window down and suck in air
Like I'm thirsty for it, watch passing cars
And try to blink away the noisy blood
Thundering in my ears, deafening me.

'When was the last time you ate anything, Yorke?'
I don't reply, try to listen to Vox,
But I can't hear over the car's engine,
Over my own blood beating at my skin.

It feels like my blood's trying to break free,
Trying to shake its way out of my veins.
Feels like my bones belong to someone else,
Like they're all at odd angles and weird shapes.

The car suddenly screeches to a halt,
Throwing me forwards into the dashboard,
Slamming my forehead against the metal.
It feels like my skull cracks from the impact.

'Shit!' Dante curses only once, sharply,
Then is silent. He's staring at something.
'What the fuck, Dante?' I groan, hold my head.
He hisses. 'Shut up. Look. Just fucking look.'

Even though my head feels like it's on fire,
My forehead like I've been hit with a brick,
I take a glance out of the front windscreen,
Then have to do a double-take, eyes wide.

It looks like the road is white and flowing.
Except, it's not. It can't be. I focus,
Try to make out what it is moving there,
And, gradually, it starts to make some sense.

Rats. Thousands of them, by the look of it.
A multitude of squirming white bodies,
Running and crawling in one long river
Of vermin across the road before us.

Dante cuts the car and I realise
That the noise I imagined was my blood
Is really the rats. They're a hellish choir,
Crying out to one another, screeching.

'What in the name of Phos…' Dante mutters.
We watch them until they finally clear,
The last of them vanishing in the dark,
Out of the car's headlight, out of our sight.

Dante turns to me. 'What the fuck was that?'
I don't know what to tell him. Just some rats?
An apparition? Some kind of white plague?
I've never seen, known, anything like it.

'Shit,' he says, and he sounds shaken, rattled,
Which is a very rare thing in Dante.
He starts the car up again and drives on,
Shuddering slightly like he's feeling cold.

I wonder what it's like to be born blind,
Like rats are; evolved to live without light.
They live out their whole lives on smell alone,
On touch, taste, sound. They don't need sight to live.

I guess maybe the rats are better off,
Living blind. Not knowing what light is like.
The blind seem to thrive in Vox. They live well,
Unencumbered by our communal greed.

There's a blind guy lives down the hall from me,
Who sits all cycle listening to music.
Sometimes I'll go round and listen with him,
Because he's the happiest guy I know.

We had a real bad case a few years back:
Some son of a bitch was blinding newborns,
And it took us way too long to catch him.
The cop who did shot him dead at the scene.
    We never found out what his motives were.
Way I saw it, the darkness made him mad;
He thought he was doing them a favour,
Saving them from the dark before they grew.
    Not that I agree with any motive
That results in blinding newborn infants.
Just that I can see how easy it is
For a sick mind to come up with that plan.
    I try to straighten the rim of my hat.
It got bent up when my head hit the car,
And I can't seem to get it back in shape.
Sometimes I wish I'd been blinded at birth.

> • <

Dante parks up alongside a meter
And digs through his pockets for change, grumbling
And slotting enough to give us an hour.
People pass us by, coats and hats held close.
    The air is tense, muggy, wind drifting warm.
Feels like there might be a storm coming soon.
Businessmen, bankers, beggars in between
All rush on, going home, finding shelter.

Here, there's a little light, enough to see
The thin bars dividing us from the ghosts
At the ends of alleyways, off from streets,
And far away from these dull sidewalk lamps.

'Darker every time I'm here,' says Dante,
Glancing around the street, locking the car.
'Sure,' I say. I don't know. I'm never here.
Even this place is too uptown for me.

He leads us against the tide of people,
Pushing a path past street vendors, salesmen.
I grab a paper from a street seller
And run my fingers across the headlines.

There's a portrait of me on page seven.
I find my features raised up in paper,
Feel the curve of the scar across my throat,
Wonder how they got it so accurate.

'Dante,' I call, and he stops, turns to me.
'Not far,' he grumbles. He looks impatient.
'No,' I say. 'We've gotta talk. The North case.'
Dante sighs. 'Not our case any more, Yorke.'

He carries on, but I catch up to him,
Stay at his shoulder. 'I know, Dante. But—'
'Forget about it, Virgil. Not our case.'
'She's missing. I couldn't find her body.'

Shouldering past a group of labourers
Looking tired, greased black faces and shovels,
Dante growls at me. 'Get your head on straight.
Somebody else is on it now, okay?'

'But they're not, Dante. Who is? Who's on it?'
'Hell if I know. Come on, quit worrying.
This. This is important. A Heart is gone.
Yorke, this could make your whole fucking career.'

My patience is badly starting to fray.
'Make your career maybe, Dante. Not mine.'
This is enough to make him stop. He frowns.
'We're not all you, Yorke. We're not all heroes.'

'I don't give a damn about my career.'
'No.' He shakes a finger at me. 'You don't.
But guess what: I do. And I've got kids, Yorke.
People who depend on me to do good.'

I open my mouth, but he interrupts,
'We can't all catch serial killers, Yorke.
I don't get many breaks on this damn job,
And I intend to find that fucking Heart.'

He stamps away before I can reply,
Nearly knocking a sweeper off his feet,
Fists clenched tight, trying to avoid listening
To anything else I might have to say.

At a shop I pick up some cigarettes,
Some ginger ale to calm my damn stomach
And a couple of cigars, one for me,
One for Dante as a peace offering.

The man behind the counter stares too long,
Recognises me, so I get out quick
And catch up to Dante along the block
Beside the huge shape of a cathedral.

It's visible only in small patches,
Lit at points by imitation candles,
Revealing huge, jagged architecture
Like light is trying to push a way out.
　　Dante's looking up at it, hesitant.
He holds this holy place in high regard:
A superstitious man, knows his scripture,
Worships on the tenth cycle, every week.
　　I've never been comfortable worshipping.
Always had the sense my prayers go nowhere,
That I'm just kneeling, talking to myself.
I've never felt the warmth of God's great love.
　　I offer Dante my peace offering
And he takes it without a look or word,
Thoughtful. 'We're here,' he says. 'This is the place.'
There's seven steps up, carved out of some stone.
　　Heading in fills me with a sort of dread,
Like my absence at church has branded me
Heretic, excommunicate, unclean.
The door is heavy, metal studded wood.
　　Inside, there's more imitation candles:
Tacky things that bear little resemblance
To the real deal. All orange filaments
Mounted in specially flame-shaped glass bulbs.
　　They've got an automated flicker, too,
Making the place tremble, lengthy shadows
Cast over everything from tall pillars,
With the walls behind hidden in darkness.

It's a nice effect, gotta give it that.
With no walls to see, makes the place endless,
Apparently vast, all attention drawn
To the bright-lit altar at the centre.

There stands Phos, our star-faced god, radiant,
Resplendent and utterly glorious,
Watching over the almost-empty pews,
Arms raised, palms up in love and acceptance.

Whoever constructed Him was inspired.
Embedded in the statue are bright lights
Radiating out from His smiling face;
The face of a brilliant burning sun.

Intricately arranged tubing glows white,
Weaved into a complex pattern, a web
Shaped like the fire and light a bright star makes,
In twists and spires all across the white stone.

We approach and it's easier to see
The offerings heaped around His bare feet;
Some burned-out batteries and burned-out bulbs,
Coils of cable and even old lighters.

There's a few folk knelt around, worshipping,
Some in the pews and some up front with us.
Their prayers are a low whispering, muttering
Out of respect for the place and their god.

Dante raises his hands up to his face
And arranges them in the sign of Phos,
Fingers become the light of His star face,
Spreading His loving illumination.

We head past the altar and further through
The cathedral, much to my great relief.
I'm glad to be away from that statue,
Away from the fierce piercing eyes of Phos.

Even back here I feel like I'm corrupt,
Like I'm an affront to this holy place.
Like the dark in my head is the devil,
The pain in my gut, getting worse, his curse.

As we walk, boots loud on the cold stone floor,
I consider begging Phos forgiveness,
To purge me clean of my resident dark,
Fill me with light brighter than any drug.

But despite my latent superstition,
I'm just not built to be a man of faith.
My head's wired wrong, I'm too close to the ground;
Too much of a sceptic to accept God.

I glance over at Dante, envious.
I wish I had his faith, his certainty
In Phos, the universe and everything.
That there's a purpose, a plan, for us all.

A dusty cleric directs us further
Through bright and richly decorated rooms,
Shelves filled up with the wealth of the holy;
Reflective icons made of glass and gold.

It's almost a sign of the times in Vox;
The rich get richer while the poor suffer,
Become ghosts and fade away in the dark.
At least our clergy can live comfortably.

We finally find who we're here to see
In an office at the end of a hall
Carpeted red, walls covered in paintings
Of Phos, lit under softly glowing bulbs.

A stocky elderly woman greets us,
Bows slightly and shows us the sign of Phos.
Dante returns the gesture. I just nod.
She's a priest, wearing His star-shaped gold badge.

'This is Lady Sophia,' says Dante.
'And Sophia, this is Inspector Yorke.'
We're bid to take seats, and I'm suspicious,
Wondering what kind of lead we're here for.

I'm suddenly caught by the idea
That this is some kind of intervention
Put together by Dante, and I twitch,
Ready to run at the first sign of 'help'.

But Sophia smiles at us, is formal,
Folds her hands. 'You didn't have to come down.
I could have told you this over the phone.
Even though it's good to see you, Dante.'

It's strange seeing Dante with Sophia.
He seems vulnerable in her presence,
Like he's at school and she's the headmistress.
He looks small, unable to meet her eye.

'Tell us what?' I ask. Dante's gone quiet.
Sophia turns her attention on me
And there's something that tells me she's clever;
Maybe her posture or the way she speaks.

'Inspector Yorke,' she says, like she's tasting
My name for its flavour across her tongue.
'I have heard and read a lot about you.'
A pause, then she says, 'I won't waste your time.

'A few hours ago, I had a visit
From a friend of mine. Please understand, though,
He's a nervous man, which is why you're here
Talking to me instead of with him now.

'This friend of mine came to me for advice.
He told me that he had seen something bad,
Something important, but quite dangerous.
He told me he saw the theft of the Heart.'

I lean forwards in my chair. 'Who did it?'
Sophia shakes her head. 'I still don't know.
When he told me that much, I advised him
To call my friend, you, Dante, straight away.

'He refused. I said that I would for him,
At which point he got scared and went to leave.
Before he did, I begged him to tell me
Who did it; that I would keep it secret.

'He shook his head, and this is what he said:
"Don't call Dante. He did it. They did it.
I saw them stealing the Heart, taking it,
And if you say anything, they'll kill me."'

I resist the urge to smile, laugh out loud,
And look to Dante for his reaction.
His eyes are wide, and he says, 'What the fuck?
He saw me taking the Heart? He saw *me*?'

Sophia says, 'That's only what he said.'
There's a quiet. I let them consider
The accusation. I have no doubts here:
Dante's innocence is not in question.

    I cough, clear my throat to break the silence.
'Sophia,' I say. 'Not meaning to pry,
But this witness you have. Is he a, uh…'
Sophia finishes my question '…ghost?

    'Yes,' she says. The tension in the room drops.
Dante curses, then apologises.
'Waste of time,' he mumbles. 'Come on, Virgil.'
We stand and make our excuses, nod thanks.

    Outside, Dante spits and curses some more.
'Complete waste of fucking time. Fucking ghosts.'
I shrug. 'Nice to be out of the office.'
We pass through thick crowds, back towards the car.

    'Hey, Virgil.' Dante ignites his cigar.
'Thanks for that, back there. For not doubting me.'
I stop. 'You didn't steal it though, did you?'
For the first time this cycle, we both laugh.

❯ • ❮

    There's a sudden bright flash in the distance
Like someone's fired a flare into the sky,
But much quicker, too fast to be a flare,
And I wonder if I imagined it.

'You see that?' I've stopped in the street to stare,
But it's gone. Nobody else has seen it.
They all carry on, eyes fixed on the ground,
Marching almost in unison away.

I'm struck by the way they look like shadows,
Like absences, voids where people should be.
I am surrounded by black silhouettes,
Another shadow among the many.

From out of nowhere a guy punches me
In the gut, hard, making me double up.
The pain is like a hot knife run through me
And I find myself struggling to inhale.

I glimpse his coat, hat, as he disappears,
Try to shout out, 'Hey! Stop!' but I just choke,
Cough heavily and try to follow him.
I stumble through thick crowds, vision swimming.

Dante's somewhere nearby. He went ahead,
But I can't spot him, can't call out to him.
The pain in my gut was bad already,
And now it feels like I've swallowed hot coals.

The crowds look more and more like silhouettes,
Like they're blending together, one shadow,
And I drift between them holding my gut
Like I'm trying to keep the pain sealed in.

I can still see his hat further ahead,
Turning to see if he's being followed,
But I keep low, hide among the shadows,
Gritting my teeth and trying to keep up.

My gun feels too heavy when I draw it,
And I can feel myself start to slow down,
Like my strength is draining away from me,
Leaking slowly out of some unplugged hole.

I push onwards past people turned shadows,
Sending a few sprawling onto concrete,
Leaves of paper whirling round in my wake,
Patches of white against the rising dark.

Feels like the city is getting darker
Around me as I falter, catch my breath
At last, coughing some nameless black fluid
And staining the street. I force myself on.

I see him turn into an alleyway,
And I catch up just in time to watch him
Climb over the fence at the end, jump down
And vanish into the consuming dark.

The world around is turning monochrome
As I stumble at last up to the fence,
Unable to raise my gun and shoot him
Because I have no strength left in my arm.

My nameless, wordless assailant is gone.
I peer unsteadily into the black
And it feels like someone glares back at me,
Maybe him, maybe ghosts, maybe no one.

'Virgil!' I hear a voice, sounds like Dante,
But a thousand kilometres away.
I turn slowly, overwhelmed by the pain,
Trying to make my mouth form a reply.

He's there at the start of the alleyway,
Looking down, shocked at something on the ground.
My knees give way at last, buckling because
There's no strength left in them, either. I kneel.
From what little light there is, I can see
A long trail of black reflective liquid
Leading away from me, meeting the street,
Like a river meandering darkly.
I look down at my hand and there's more there,
Staining the bandages and my fingers.
I drop my revolver and try to stand,
But I have no more control of myself.
'Dante,' I call out as my vision fades.
'I think that's my blood. I think he stabbed me.'
Through the pain, I feel Dante pick me up,
And then nothing at all. I join the dark.

❯ • ❮

Funny where your mind goes when you're dying.
My eyes are fixed on the dining table,
A single corner of the cloth cover
Where there's a lipstick stain, scarlet on white.
And I'm wondering if it'll wash out,
If my wife will take it to the laundrette
Or if we're gonna need a new cover.
All I see is that scarlet lipstick stain.

She wears it each cycle, her favourite shade;
I've memorised the way she smiles, so red.
She's got her very own noose beside mine,
And it doesn't occur to me she's dead.

THIRD CYCLE

'It's time for you to wake, Inspector Yorke.'
Feels like I've been run over by a train.
My eyes refuse to open when I try.
That's fine; I can see the room anyway.
    There's some dark shapes, but it's mostly brightness
Forcing its way past my eyelids. At last,
I manage to get a glimpse of the place.
All wealth; I'm lying in a four-poster.
    'You are lucky to have such a wise friend,'
Continues the voice that dragged me from sleep.
'He was clever enough to bring you here.'
I turn my head and feel my neck complain.
    'Water?' There's a man with me, got dark skin,
And though my memory's all broken-up,
I think I recognise him, who he is.
Cancer offers me a glass of water.

I'm croaking, rasping, trying to sit up,
But my throat feels as rough as sandpaper,
And the pain in my stomach holds me down.
'Where am I?' I manage, sipping water.

'Good question,' he says. His eyes are dark, too;
Two pools of black circled with glinting white.
'You're in my house, inspector. "The Lighthouse",
It's called. Do you know what a lighthouse is?'

The water makes me choke, splutter, wretched,
The movement making my gut strike fresh pain
Through me, like I've been stabbed over again.
Cancer takes the water from me, explains,

'A long, long time ago people used them
To guide boats away from rocky waters.
They would light towers like this up, brightly:
Enormous candles at the top of cliffs.'

He continues on while I remember
What happened. The feel of the knife through me.
My fingers run across the wound, bound tight,
Metal staples holding my insides in.

'We come from a place where light isn't rare,
You see. Where things like wood, matches and gas
All burn not quite as hot, but visibly.
Can you imagine light so abundant?

'It seems almost wasteful, don't you think, Yorke?
May I call you Virgil? Is that okay?
You lost a lot of blood. How are you now?
I had my best man come and repair you.'

They must have put me on strong painkillers,
Because my head feels better than ever,
Like I'm floating among clouds in the sky.
'Sure,' I manage. 'Thanks. I feel... great, I guess.'

'Good,' he says. His dark skin confuses me.
He looks strange, like a shadow come alive.
'Now, where was I? Ah, of course. The Lighthouse.
This place is a lighthouse like no other.

'Once upon a time this house burned brightly,
But not for simple sailing boats, oh no,
For boats capable of crossing the stars.
To warn them, "Stay away from that dark world!"

'My lighthouse is no longer lit, Virgil,
Because there are no more boats to warn off.
Five hundred years ago we landed here,
And five hundred years ago we, well... stopped.

'And now what do we have left of all that?
Remnants. Old lightbulbs, a last few candles,
And the objects used to power those boats,
The Hearts. Three of them. And mine is missing.'

His face changes, creases, becomes annoyed.
'You and I both know you're being set up.
You're an addict, and now you've been injured.
But you're the luckiest fool that I know.

'There's a reason I asked for you, Virgil.
You're something of a lucky charm to me.
You see, I lost someone to the Hangman.
And you, you lucky fool, well, you stopped him.

'I've seen the reports. I know what happened
Back then. You're a hero because of luck,
And I need you to be lucky again.
I need you to return my Heart to me.

'Of course your chief, Garfield, is in on it.
There will be a lot of money involved.
Remember, Virgil, there are two more Hearts,
And two other jealous owners like me.

'The press, the papers are saying one thing,
But I'm saying that it was one of them.
Aquila, Corvus: one of them did it.
One of them paid to have Cancer stolen.'

It's a lot to take in, but filled with drugs,
My mind feels sharper. I process quickly
While he helps me out of bed. I'm quite weak,
Legs trembling, but I can just about stand.

'I'm going to let you back out, Virgil,
But that stabbing was not an accident.
You're a target, my friend. You're being watched.
They're relying on you being a fool.

'In fact, I'm counting on you to be one.
I need you to be a fool. Just lucky.
Be my lucky charm and find my Heart, please.
And when you do, don't tell them. Come to me.'

He helps me into some pants and a shirt,
Buttons it up for me, finds me some shoes,
Ties the laces. Then he grabs my arm tight
And pushes a needle into a vein.

I don't know what it is, but it's not Pro'.
It's a clear liquid that makes me awake,
So awake, and completely free of pain.
I could hop and skip out of here right now.

'I have another gift for you,' he says,
Unlocking a heavy wooden cupboard.
I'm busy feeling like a dynamo,
On the biggest caffeine kick of my life.

In a moment, I've taken the place in.
The room is extravagant, filled with lights,
Walls covered floor to ceiling in mirrors,
Chandeliers like huge clusters of diamonds.

Everything here is coated in silver,
From the dressers, the chairs, even the floor,
Which is covered in a silver carpet.
Everything is reflective and shining.

'Here,' says Cancer, and then I realise
That his skin makes him the only shadow
In the room. The only piece of darkness.
He's holding a cigarette out to me.

Feeling like a million bucks, I grin,
Take the cigarette, place it in my mouth.
There's something about the taste already,
Some strange flavour I've never met before.

'Enjoy,' he says, and ignites it for me.
'There's not many of those left any more.'
I inhale, and it's like tasting colour,
Brilliant, deep, rich, and impossible.

I forget to exhale until he says,
'Check the end, Virgil,' lifting an ashtray.
I do, and there's light there. Glowing embers.
I've never seen glowing embers before.

Some part of me not caught up in the high
Tells me that this cigarette is special.
I put it out, find something to wrap it
And slip it, careful, into a pocket.

Cancer is simply stood there, watching me,
Smiling at my reaction. 'Time to go,'
He tells me. 'Go and find my Heart, Virgil.
You have six hours until that shot wears off.'

On light feet I am guided through the house,
Past bowing servants and endless hallways.
At the front doors, someone hands me my coat
And hat, freshly laundered, smelling real sweet.

'Oh,' Cancer says, as I step into Vox.
'Inspector.' He looks serious again.
'If I find out that you've taken Promo'
Again, I will end your life. Understand?'

I smile and nod at him, reassuring,
And watch as the doors to the Lighthouse close.
I admire the slender line of light there,
Getting thinner until it vanishes.

> • <

The papers have turned mad, almost frantic.
Someone's spilled the news that the Hearts are bombs,
And it gets worse as I read down the page,
Religious extremists getting involved.

Threats and demands are being made by all:
Manifestos claiming Phos is evil,
Or that Phos hates us, wants us all to die,
Or that we just plain don't love Phos enough.

A few groups are even making big claims,
That they have the Heart, that it's their weapon,
That the whole city is at their mercy.
The paper stinks of confusion, panic.

Any one of those groups might have the Heart,
Or maybe it's one of Cancer's rivals,
Or anyone else in the damn city.
For all I know, could be that I took it.

I have a rare moment of clarity,
Stood halfway down a busy block in town,
Paper at hand, watching faces pass by.
I realise just how alone I am.

Cancer reckons my department's corrupt,
In on it, and if he's right then that means
Vox is on the verge of going to hell
And I'm the only one stood in the way.

I drop the paper and look at the sky,
Look at all those points of light up there: stars,
And wonder why ours is the way it is,
The only dark star among the countless.

I pull my collar up to hide the scar,
Hail a cab from the edge of the sidewalk
And check my revolver: four bullets left.
I direct the driver into the dark.

> • <

'Where you headed?' The driver coasts the streets.
I'm huddled up on the leather back seat,
Rolling a coin round between my fingers.
It's a good question. Truth is, I don't know.
    The cab's a rattling piece of junk, jarring
My thoughts. Cracked, dusty windows, clouded up
By the warmth of my breath, hide the city.
Can't tell where he's driving, where we're going.
    I hold the coin up to my eyes, see it
Glint, catching the edge of the cab's headlight.
Heads for Corvus and tails for Aquila.
One of them's gotta know something, surely.
    The cabbie watches the coin spin with me,
Caught by the tip of my thumb, flicked up high,
Just short of the cab's shaking canvas roof.
I snatch it out of the air, catch it clean
    And hold it tight, fingers wrapped around it.
Heads for Corvus and tails for Aquila.
I spend too long staring at my closed hand.
'You gonna check that, friend?' asks the cabbie.

Funny, the way you know which side you want
The coin to come down when it's in the air.
I keep my hand closed, put the coin away.
'Uptown,' I say. 'Take me to the Uni'.'

> • <

I pull the handle and lo and behold,
The door swings open. My lucky cycle.
I tug the keys out from the ignition
And take a quick look about the dark lot.

There's no Uni' staff around to stop me
From giving it a closer look over.
Call it a hunch or whatever you like,
But something bothered me about this car.

Last time I was here I couldn't place it.
But now I'm back, haunting the empty lot,
I know what it is. The make and model:
Same kind I saw dead outside the North house.

This one's got two headlights over the grill,
One empty, like the car's blind in one eye.
It's a mess, nearly more rust than metal,
But could be the Norths collect these old cars.

There's a chance I'm wrong. I don't trust myself.
Could be I'm joining dots that just aren't there.
But right now I'm thinking that this car here
Belongs, or belonged, to Vivian North.

Balancing my dull torch on the dashboard,
I check under the seats and the glove box,
Turning up a whole lot of nothing. Dust.
Two cigarette stubs in a black ashtray.

I back out, ignite my own and inhale.
Guess I was expecting an easy clue,
Some sign of a struggle, maybe some blood.
The car's as clean as a fresh alibi.

I try the trunk last, hauling it open.
There's a bunch of dark shapes inside, boxes,
And it takes me a while, cuffing my torch,
To get enough light in there to see by.

Looks like notes. Hell of a lot of them, too.
I rifle through, running my fingers down
Barely legible scribbled lines. Class notes.
History class. I find her name, at least.

Getting involved in absorbing the notes,
I don't notice that my nose is bleeding
Until the blood is running down my face,
Dripping dark patches across white paper.

I wad some useless sheets and press them up,
Catching the blood and trying to ignore
The blunt ache returning to my stomach
And the hunger there, barely kept at bay.

It takes my torch dying for me to think,
To wake up and realise there's nothing
In the notes. They're just academia.
A part of her course. They're empty of use.

I throw the papers I've gone through back in
And take a breather, leaning on the car.
Running a finger across the stab wound
Makes it sting. Cancer's shot is wearing off.

In a surge of frustration, I throw notes
To either side, sifting through them, searching
For anything. The papers just slide back.
Feels like I'm hunting for a grain in sand.

My fingers brush up against something hard.
There's a shape among the papers. A case,
Made of leather. It fits into my palm,
About the same size as a piece of fruit.

With my torch out of juice, I can't see it.
I run my hands over it, find the catch,
Open it up and try to understand
What comes tumbling out. I almost drop it.

Feels like paper, but not paper. Plastic.
It's a reel of camera film: negatives.
I hold the film between my hands and laugh.
It hurts, but I laugh, relieved, anyway.

Could be anything at all on that film.
As far as I'm concerned, it's a good sign,
That I haven't just wasted my time here.
I coil it, careful, back into its case.

Locking the car's boot and each of the doors,
I pocket the keys. Pays to be cautious.
Leather case in hand, I head towards light,
Out of the black lot and up a stone ramp.

Security check me over again,
Even though I was here two cycles past.
Huge men with short memories pat me down,
Squinting at my badge like it's counterfeit.

I'll never get used to the lights in here.
The University is way too bright,
Naked bulbs making me vulnerable
Out of the dark, leaving nowhere to hide.

She's there at the front desk, just like I'd hoped.
'Inspector Yorke,' she says. 'Good to see you.'
This time, when Rachel smiles, it's personal,
Like she's genuinely glad to see me.

'Thought I'd drop by,' I tell her. My shadow
Is draped across the white floor beside me,
At least twice my height, my echo in dark.
Hard to look at her. I keep my eyes low.

'You're here to see the professor,' she says
Matter of fact, like she can read my mind.
I follow her and become her shadow,
Treading down long halls empty of students.

He's not in. Hasn't been for a cycle.
Rachel opens his office anyway,
Leans against the frame of the door, watching
Me open drawers I'm not meant to open.

'He's done something, hasn't he?' Rachel says.
I find what I'm looking for in his desk.
It's heavy, an awkward shape, made of glass
And metal. 'What's that?' she asks. 'What is that?'

'You've sure got a lot of questions,' I say.
Rachel shrugs, smiles, tilts her head, observes me
And plays with the set of keys she's holding.
'I can't work you out, Virgil,' she tells me.

There's the idol of Phos still on its shelf
And I turn it around before leaving,
Averting His gaze from my act of theft,
Stealing the professor's Heart replica.

'Let him know I want a word,' I tell her
As she locks his office, leading us back
To reception and beyond, heels clicking.
My tongue feels like it's been tied into knots.

'Don't be a stranger, inspector,' she says
At the door, and it causes me to pause,
Heart in hand, halfway between bright and black.
I turn around, but she's already gone.

> • <

I stride through the city in the darkness,
Hat tipped like I'm hiding my eyes from it.
In one hand I have the Heart replica,
And in the other, the camera film reel.

At a crossroads I stop, watch passing cars,
Barely visible vehicles rumbling,
Little more than wavering cones of light,
Flashing windscreens, pale faces, white knuckles.

There's a ghost across the way, chasing them,
Fingers curling uselessly around glows,
There for fleeting moments, then vanishing.
The wild, wide whites of his eyes are glinting.

Igniting a cigarette, I observe
A quick two-seater clip him, throwing him
Bodily onto the sidewalk, broken,
Slender limbs unmoving, any cry masked.

I stamp the stub of the cigarette out,
Crush it beneath my boot, and carry on.
Funny to think that without Vox's Hearts,
We would all be turned to that. Less than dead.

> • <

Wilson's place is down a quiet back street.
I locate it by running my fingers
Across closed shop fronts and locked-up doorways
Until they meet the curled number sixty.

Number sixty at the back of nowhere;
Doesn't look like Wilson is doing well.
Still, it's discretion I'm needing right now.
There's a bell-pull beneath the shop number.

No amount of ringing, of loud knocking,
Summons the man. Guess it's past trading hours.
I make myself comfortable on the step,
Rummage around for some paper, a pen.

I scrawl a message for him on a scrap;
Disassembling the words, mouthing letters
And pressing them backwards across the note.
Always something I struggled with in school.
　　When he finds it, he'll read the other side;
The ridges formed of the valleys I make,
Fingers making sense of the words I write
Backwards now, licking the tip of the pen.
　　'Need these developed quick. Thanks – Virgil Yorke.'
I check it to make sure it's legible,
Then slip it into the leather film case,
Pushing it inside through the hinged mail slot.

❯ • ❮

Halfway down a block, I notice the noise
Made by the guy following me. His steps
Are almost in time with mine, but softer.
He's listening out for me in the darkness.
　　What gives him away is the way he stops
Every time I do, quiet to hear me,
And when I continue on, so does he.
We're caught together in a kind of dance.
　　There's some twinkling in the dark up ahead;
Some lights that mark my transition away
From these unseen streets to brighter districts,
Made aglow for patrons blessed with some wealth.

I lead my tail on through gathering crowds,
A mix of ghosts being kept separate
And ordinary folk heading uptown,
Streaming on through the open gates ahead.

I'll be damned if I'm getting stabbed again.
I take my time, pretend I've not noticed,
Queue up with the rest and find my ID.
I can lose my tail on the other side.

The men on security look tired, bored,
Barely glance at my ID, at my badge.
It's easy to distinguish Vox's ghosts
From the rest. There's a hunger about them.

I need to find a corner to hide in,
Somewhere I can back up against a wall,
Draw my revolver and keep watch over
The crowds; try and spot who's following me.

People pass by without a single glance,
Caught up in their own lives, eyes wide open,
Staring lustily up at the street lamps,
Barely paying each other attention.

Striding down the street and through open doors,
I enter a busy establishment,
Shoulder-to-shoulder with men wearing suits
And women in sparkling, sequinned dresses.

There's laughter in the air, endless voices,
Shouting, clacking, the crisp scent of fresh cash,
And the kind of musk I associate
With greedy and desperate people: gamblers.

Looks like I've walked into a casino.
I carry on between black felt tables,
Cards and faces lit by dim glowing bulbs,
White dice and white teeth reflecting the light.

Hunched figures perch on tall stools, some standing
Instead, all looming over dark tables.
Chips sweep away, dollars changing owners,
Victors hissing, clapping, cheering, eyes wide.

They haven't bothered with a bulb above.
All attention is drawn to the tables,
To the stakes, the spin of the glowing wheel,
The turn of the cards, the roll of the dice.

I head towards the back of the wide room,
To the darkest recesses of the place,
Passing a weeping man, empty pockets,
And a quiet bar, empty of patrons.

There, I find the edge of a couch and wait,
Watching out for any kind of approach.
A puzzled-looking man joins me, ignites
A cigarette, stares at his empty hands.

'The wife's gonna leave me,' he says, softly.
I shake my head, frown, try to say nothing,
But I don't get it. I don't get this place.
'Why are you here, then? Why gamble it all?'

His eyes are just as empty as his hands.
He looks at me without understanding,
As if he had no choice in the matter.
As if his money ran away from him.

Someone else approaches, in uniform.
Looks like a member of staff. She's smiling,
But it's polite. 'Hi, Mister Yorke,' she says.
'You're expected upstairs. Follow me, please.'

I don't take my hand away from my gun.
'You're gonna have to explain,' I tell her.
'You're expected,' she repeats, politely.
'You have an appointment upstairs, right now.'

Two huge men seem to materialise
From the dark to stand either side of her,
Each easily the size of a phone booth.
I remove my hand from my revolver.

Doesn't look like I have much of a choice.
Trying to conceal the Heart replica,
I follow the girl back through the packed room
And up a wide flight of dimly lit steps.

We reach a heavy-looking door and stop.
I'm told to wait outside, and the two goons
Take the opportunity to search me.
They find both the replica and the gun.

Of course, when I'm finally ushered through,
My two new friends come with me, looking stern.
They haven't quite introduced themselves yet,
But I've got great names for them in my head.

This room looks and feels a lot like downstairs,
But private. There's only one table here.
The first thing to catch my eye is the stakes;
They're betting batteries at this table.

It's lit by a low-hanging ring of light
At eye-level, yellow and comfortable,
Causing jewellery, nails and cards to glow,
As if they're producing some light themselves.

I'm led round to one of the game's players
And deposited there, stood in the dark,
Wishing I was anywhere else right now
And cursing my luck. I watch the next hand.

When it's done, he turns to me, hard to see.
His silhouette is broad, and he looks bald,
But that's just about all I can make out.
When he speaks, his voice is deep, accent strong.

'Mister Yorke,' he drawls. 'Real nice to meet you.'
One of my hands is twitching, so I clench
It tight, clench my jaw tight, try to ignore
The pain in my gut, slowly worsening.

'You wanted to talk to me?' I ask him.
'Sure,' he says. 'You and I share an interest.
Thought it might be worth us having a chat.
Face to face, friendly like. Please, take a seat.'

The girl returns with a chair, and I sit,
Caught in conversation with the bald man.
The game goes on quietly behind him,
A complex network of slow exchanges.

'Thanks,' I say. 'How can I help you then, sir?'
'You can knock that off right away,' he says.
'While in here, you're not a man of the law.
You're just Yorke. Mister Yorke. You understand?

'I'm hoping that you and I can be friends.
Good friends, who can help each other out. See,
I'm a resourceful, influential man,
And you… you are a man in need of help.'

  I'm beginning to get the impression
That my coming in here was no mistake.
Maybe my tail was one of this guy's men.
I get to the point. 'What is it you want?'

  He sighs through his nose. 'I want Cancer's Heart.
I want you to find it, bring it to me
And walk away a very wealthy man.
Clear enough? I want Cancer, Mister Yorke.'

  I'm in no position to say no. 'Sure.
The Heart. Whatever you want. Who are you?'
This causes him to chuckle. 'You don't know?
You should talk with your DEA friends more.

  'I'm a man of many means, Mister Yorke,
And one of them is the distribution
Of a narcotic called Prometheus.
I'm a drug baron, Yorke. A real bad man.

  'I've got friends who call me "The Hand of Phos",
But you can call me Shepherd. I'm Shepherd,
And right now I'm offering you money.
A lot of money. More money than Phos.'

  I do recognise the name, but right now
I can't place it. Some news column, maybe.
My blood is surging strange, palpitations
Making me twitch at the mention of Pro'.

'And if it's not money you're wanting, well,
I'm sure I can provide… other rewards.'
Ah, hell. Does everyone in this city
Know I'm addicted to Prometheus?

He quits talking at me, leaves the offer
In the quiet for me to consider,
Like I have any choice in the matter.
'Sure,' I say. 'I'm gonna need your help, though.'

He claps his hands together, rubbing them.
'I knew you and I would see eye to eye.
You're not as dense as I'm told, Mister Yorke.
Any help you need, name it and it's yours.'

I figure I might as well use Shepherd.
It's not like I have any other leads.
'I'm gonna need my things back,' I tell him.
'And anything you might have heard yourself.'

'These ears hear a lot of interesting things,
But I'd wager what you're needing to know
Is that I don't know whoever did it.
And trust me, I know a lot of people.

'If there was a bounty put on the Heart,
Then you and I would not be chatting now.
Which leaves two possibilities: the cops,
Or our fine military. Take your pick.'

Looks like Shepherd's had the same idea
As Cancer. A police operation.
Well that's just great, exactly what I need,
Having to investigate my own kind.

There's the Corruption Department, of course,
But they're a big joke. They're corrupt themselves.
Cops don't snitch on other cops as a rule;
Everyone's got dirt on everyone else.

    I wring my hat between my hands and say,
'All right,' and then, because I'm curious,
'Don't suppose you've heard about this dead girl,
Vivian North, found veins full of glowing?'

    There's a pause as he considers her name.
'Prometheus?' he asks. 'No,' I reply.
'Never heard of her. How's she relevant?'
I shrug, not sure of that question myself.

    I stand. 'Guess we're done then, Mister Shepherd.'
He doesn't shake my hand. 'You keep in touch,'
He says. 'Leave me any messages here.'
His goons, like two moving statues, guide me

    Away through the dark, his voice following:
'Double-cross me and I'll see the next knife
Tears that smile across your neck right open.
I hope to hear from you soon, Mister Yorke.'

    Looks like I'm making a fine collection
Of threats this cycle. So many nooses
Around my neck it hurts to bow my head.
Inside, I'm hanging, choking already.

    They push me through a back door and down steps
Made of dripping, rusted metal, creaking
Under my weight, and hand me my things back:
My gun, the Heart model, and something else.

Among the heaps of trash in the alley
I unwrap Shepherd's glowing parting gift.
Son of a bitch has given me Promo'.
Seven full phials of the fucking stuff.

I curse his name every way I know how,
And then my own because I can't drop them.
I can't throw them away. I need this shit
Because without it I'm a fucking wreck.

When I'm done swearing at Shepherd, Cancer,
Garfield and even poor damn Vivian,
And I'm all out of insults, I hiss and
Nearly crush the phials between my fingers.

I imagine the warm liquid leaking,
Running, dripping down my wrists, down my arms,
And I feel a strong rush of vertigo.
My body won't let me waste the damn stuff.

Instead, I pocket the Prometheus,
Making sure there's no glint, no shine showing,
And rejoin the masses in the main street,
Feeling a sharp stab of pain from my wound.

Guess it's been close to six hours since Cancer
Gave me that shot. I'm starting to feel bad.
It's no worse than my normal cravings, though.
Nothing I can't handle with willpower.

I figure it's about time I go find
The only guy whose name I haven't cursed.
Pressing my free hand to my aching gut,
I walk Vox, hunting my partner: Dante.

> • <

I walk astride the sea front, following
My shadow as it is: struck before me
Across the concrete sidewalk, made moving
By the slow stream of traffic beside me.

    I'm another figure among many,
Coat drawn close against the spray of the sea,
Glittering, faceted flecks of ocean
Throwing themselves at us as we pass by.

    The storm that's been brewing two cycles now
Is close. There's a rising wind in the warm
And a tension with it: a dark promise.
Knowing my luck, I'll be caught out in it.

    Headquarters is just ahead, down the road.
It's there that I hope to locate Dante
And catch up with the case I'm neglecting;
Probably about time I chase the Heart.

    Two blocks away from my destination
And my luck, just as expected, runs out.
Sometimes I reckon that I'm still paying
For crimes I committed in a past life.

    The roadblock looks like it's routine enough:
Officers going about their business
Among the flashing red lights, the cars parked
To make sure everyone's checked as they pass.

There's a bunch of uniforms taking names,
But the guys who spot me are wearing coats,
Wide hats, silver badges and concealed guns.
They're smiling like they've won the lottery.

'Yorke, right?' says one, hand placed on my shoulder,
And before I've worked out what's happening
They've got me over the hood of a car,
Going through my pockets. 'Hey! What the fuck?'

'Shut the fuck up.' It doesn't take them long
To find the bag full of Prometheus,
Grab the rest of my stuff, force me to kneel,
Slap a pair of bracelets around my wrists.

'What the fuck are you doing? I'm a cop!'
'You're a fucking junkie, is what you are.'
One waves the bag. 'Ten years for this, I'd say.'
'I'm a fucking detective, you morons!'

The written reports will say I fought back,
That they had to beat me in self-defence.
Hell, I've beat a few crooks in cuffs before,
But the kicks to my chest feel personal.

And when they're done, they haul me to my feet,
Drag me round and throw me in a squad van
To bleed. I get a glance at the markings:
DEA. Fucking great. They're Drug Squad cops.

Through the pain in my gut, my new bruises
And the wretched hunger under my skin,
I manage to see the humour in it.
This cycle's been one long bad joke on me.

I shuffle back into a black corner
And try to not die as the van starts up,
Knocking me from wall to wall as it goes.
I concentrate on the pain to stay sharp.

> • <

We learn quick: fire is fucking dangerous.
When the air in the city gets this close,
People get twitchy, tend to run and hide
Away from high spires and open spaces.
    One bad lightning strike and the city burns.
How are you meant to fight what you can't see?
A really big blaze, you can feel the heat,
Get blinded by the smog, the writhing smoke,
    But something smaller, the strike of a match,
There's nothing to see; no way of knowing.
Hold a flame up to light, you might notice
Fluttering heat in the air, but that's it.
    Stories say that stars are made of bright flames,
That old candles burn with visible fire,
That the face of Phos is a shining blaze,
But I can't imagine a flame like that.
    Fire is the destroyer, the great absence.
It devours, turns brightness into blackness,
Swallows all the progress we people make
And shits out nothing but ruins, ashes.

I watched a guy as he burned to death once,
Watched the heat rising from his searing flesh,
His skin peeling itself back, blood steaming,
Open mouth streaming white smoke. A slow death.

Nobody dared get close to help the guy.
No telling where the fire was in the place;
Its wretched effects were all we could see.
We formed a perimeter near the heat.

And when the firemen arrived, it was done;
Everything was already burned away.
They still chucked some water on in buckets.
Just in case, they said to us. Just in case.

Big men wearing big coats and hard helmets:
They're just as helpless as the rest of us.
One bad lightning strike and the city burns;
We all burn; our whole fucking world burns down.

> • <

The arms around me are enough to wake
Me from my delirium, caught in thoughts
Of fire, thunder, rain and lightning: the storm.
They drag me out from the back of the van.

Warm rain soothes my skin, washes my bruises,
Soaks through my broken coat, into my boots.
I'm too weak to walk, so they carry me
Between themselves, like I'm a sack of flesh.

There's nobody watching the pilgrimage.
Nobody to stop them as they take me
Across the dark lot, through the rising storm
And towards a glimmering white lantern.

They discuss where they should be holding me,
And the consensus is that I'm a corpse
And should be put with the rest of the dead.
They let my feet drag down every damn step.

We begin our descent, through open doors
And past shadowed, inhabited chambers
Divided from us by vertical bars,
Housing wasted and crooked silhouettes.

Our journey to the bowels of the station
Takes us past other officers, tall men
Rattling the cages of addicts, dealers,
Each busy awaiting trial or release.

The wasted faces behind those black bars
Have a hunger I recognise: my own.
I see me a hundred times, reflected
Worse than any mirror; I see myself.

The lights get worse the deeper we go down,
Slowly spiralling past the station's pens,
Until the addicts become skeletons,
Bones covered in thin skin, barely breathing.

We pass the last bulb, a cracked dim beacon,
And a flickering torch is lit instead,
For the last set of steps, rusted railings
Leading us into the deepest darkness.

Here, there's a stench, like panic, like cattle
Penned in too close together. Animal.
Those crouched behind the bars don't look alive:
A network of spindly limbs gathered up.

Yet, they stir under the gaze of the torch,
Unfolding themselves, crying out weakly,
Begging for another lick of the light.
They're the restless almost-dead: Vox's ghosts.

Hard to tell how many there are down here.
Maybe hundreds. They stink like a thousand.
The sweep of the torch reveals more and more,
Huddled up together, wrapped in torn rags.

Those with some remaining sense shuffle back
As the door to their cage opens outwards,
But some crawl forwards, fingers uncurling,
Only to be kicked back, out of the way.

They drop me in there like an offering,
Their laughter echoing around the cage.
'Try to get some sleep, Yorke. We'll be back soon.'
The door rattles shut behind me, key turned.

They leave, and I am surrounded by dark,
The dead shuffling, whimpering and stinking,
Fingers searching me for food, for stray glows,
But I'm dark. I have no light left for them.

My hunger is absolute. A huge weight
Pressing down on my chest, consuming me.
I'm craving Prometheus. Any light.
The tiniest reprieve from my shadows.

There's a sticky damp around my stab wound
That's probably blood, mingling with the rain
Clinging on to my coat, into my skin.
My head's too full of craving to feel hurt.

 I'm holding on to consciousness, awake
But wondering how, how I carry on.
Even here, in the depths of hell, I live.
Maybe I'm just too damn stubborn to die.

 I find some strength and push myself backwards
Until I find a wall, sat in some damp
Between spindly bodies twitching, dying,
And lament my lost hat. I liked that hat.

 Without my everycycle dose of Pro',
A brand new hell confronts me: withdrawals.
These cravings now are nothing when compared
With the hours ahead. I'm starting to sweat.

 Soon, that sweat will turn to shaking, wracking
Pains, and a consuming delirium.
I've seen it happen to other addicts.
Never seen one make it through. They give in.

 My itching thoughts search for a solution,
Desperately trying to find me a fix,
And they come across possibility.
Something to ease the pain of passing through.

 I search my pockets and find the tissue
Wrapped around Cancer's gift. The cigarette.
By some divine luck, it's intact and dry.
I spend a moment giving thanks to Phos.

Of course I don't have a fucking dry match.
They're all soaked and made useless by the rain.
I hang the cigarette between my lips
And catch the smallest sample of its taste.

'Hey,' I say, and my voice sounds hoarse, broken.
Still, the whimpering and weeping stops short.
The ghosts are listening. Well I'll be damned, then.
'Don't suppose any of you've got a flame?'

There's a shuffling sound, the ghosts moving round,
Repositioning themselves to hear me.
I don't understand why. 'You know, a match?'
Maybe it's been a while since they heard speech.

There's the noise of more movement around me,
And some spindly collection of fingers
Winds its way up my arm, locates my hand
And presses something there, something tiny.

I roll it between my fingers to feel
And it's such a small thing. A slight remnant.
Some ghost has just given me a match head.
The quiet in the cage is expectant.

I can feel the bad tremors beginning
Under my skin, and my heart protesting,
Demanding liquid light. To hell with it.
I find a rough patch of concrete to use.

It takes one quick motion to strike the match,
And I can feel the flame burning my hand,
But I hold it up to the cigarette
And inhale before it can disappear.

The flavour fills me. It tastes like it glows:
Warm, a comfort, a small point of wonder.
And by the glowing of its strange embers
I can see the glinting of all their eyes.

They're gathered around me, completely still,
Hypnotised by it. My congregation
Of ghosts, caught up in the same strange wonder.
None of them make a move to snatch it up.

For the next few moments I'm at the edge,
Hanging on to my last seconds of light
And looking down at the oblivion,
The blackness waiting to swallow me up.

The ghosts are whispering among themselves
And it might be language, but I'm not sure.
I don't care. I hold on to the feeling,
To the cigarette, until it's all gone.

Only then, I fall down inside myself,
Into the blackest recesses of me,
Lost in my ravenous, howling hunger
And the pain pushing its way through my veins.

> • <

I drag his bleeding body for three blocks
Until a routine patrol picks me up.
I'd have called them, but my throat is messed up,
A ragged smile drawn across it in blood.

They tell me I shot the Hangman six times
With his own gun, emptied it into him,
But I don't remember. All I recall
Is the long walk, the weight of his body.
I think I planned to take him to the sea,
Weigh him down and watch him sink in the dark,
But it's not clear. I'm not quite thinking straight;
Painting three blocks of sidewalk in his blood.

FOURTH **CYCLE**

'You got a spare smoke, Dante? I'm all out.'
Except, it's not Dante driving the car,
Just someone who looks a lot like he does,
Hunched behind the wheel like the car's too small.

    The driver passes me a cigarette,
But the damn thing won't stay between my lips.
I watch it tumble down under my seat
And I'm helpless, can't follow it, too weak.

    'I'll call Dante when we get in,' says Fife.
I recognise his voice, deep like it is.
'You rest up, Yorke. Looks like you've been through hell.
You're lucky I caught wind you'd been brought in.'

    We pass a bunch of trucks, and they light up
The city around us: trash everywhere,
Gutters full, overflowing in the wake
Of the big storm. Looks like I missed the worst.

I notice I'm not shaking any more,
That I'm not sweating and heaving, bleeding;
That the skin across my hands seems darker,
Like it's lost the glow that used to be there.

I'm left with a sort of black hollowness
Instead. Like someone's taken my insides
And thrown them out. Like you could open me
And there would be nothing to see: darkness.

Guess I'm free of the withdrawals, at least.
Fife turns a corner down a dark district
I don't recognise, through the last light rain.
'Thanks,' I say. And then, 'Where are we going?'

Fife squints out at the road. 'Back to my place.
I wouldn't normally, but what the hell,
The wife's at work and the kids are at school.
And you need a shower, my friend. You stink.'

I don't disagree. 'Yeah,' I say. 'Sounds good.'
'Look,' he says. 'The guys that arrested you.
They've got a rep' for corruption. I think
Someone paid them to have you taken in.'

'Report them,' I tell him. 'Pair of lowlives.'
'Yeah, I would,' he says, 'but they wouldn't care.
One's the stepson of a commissioner.
More trouble than it's worth, if you ask me.

'And hell, looks like they did you a favour.'
'A favour?' 'You damn well know what I mean.'
I'm too exhausted to put up a fight.
'Clocked it the moment I set eyes on you.'

We spend the rest of the drive in silence,
Skirting the suburbs, low-rise apartments
And semi-detached ruins barely lit.
He pulls into a driveway, glares at me.

'You were never here, okay?' he tells me.
'Sure.' He helps me onto my feet and stoops
To keep one arm around my waist. My feet
Refuse to follow orders. I stumble.

In the dark of his house, he runs some taps,
Screws a bulb into the bathroom socket
And leaves me a rough-looking robe, a towel,
And a promise to burn my clothes after.

It takes me a while to remove my shirt.
My fingers fumble around the buttons,
But the worst is where my wound's been leaking,
Dried blood and vomit encrusting the cloth.

One hand after another, I lower
Myself into the water and sink down,
Watching filth rise up from all parts of me;
Feeling the sting of the heat as it hits.

I let it drain away, watch it running
Down the plughole, my swirling filth fleeing,
And switch the shower on instead, huddled
In the corner of the tub in a heap.

There, I run a hand down my pointed ribs
Where they jut around my sunken stomach,
Notice how skeletal I am right now,
How much I must look as if I'm starving.

All those cycles in my dark apartment
And I never noticed myself wasting
Away, hooked bad on the Prometheus
And fading one little shot at a time.

My face against the base of the bathtub,
I heave the last of myself, black mucus
Trailing from my mouth until I'm empty.
Then, there's nothing left. I have nothing left.

There's the flickering bulb and I watch it,
Buzzing and humming, set in the ceiling.
Wonder how close I am to vanishing,
To becoming another ghost in Vox.

The robe is roughly twice as big as me,
But it's warm. The heat of the water lit
A fire in me, gave me a little strength:
Enough to stand, enough to walk; to breathe.

Fife's waiting in the kitchen with some pie,
'Yestercycle's remains,' he says to me.
I hand him his bulb, still warm, still glowing,
And dig in. Turns out I'm pretty hungry.

'Look,' he says, 'I was gonna get in touch.
Got something you might be interested in.'
I drain a glass of water, another,
And profess my undying gratitude.

'Sure.' He waves me off, but he's smiling some.
'But you remember the North girl, don't you?'
I stop eating. 'Sure do. What about her?'
He shrugs. 'Something about her bothered me.'

'Her case has gone walkabout,' I tell him,
And he's the first guy yet who gives a damn.
'Yeah. That bothered me too. Not quite right, that.
Nobody's got a clue where her case went.'

I finish the pie and flex my fingers,
Feel the life flushing back through to the tips.
'So what? You been looking into it too?'
He shakes his head, shuffles the bulb around.

'I put my nose where it doesn't belong,
My department, I get that nose cut off.
My family can't take that kinda shit.'
We both glance at the dull bulb above us.

'Ah, to hell with it. If you still care, Yorke,
Then maybe this'll help.' He strides across
To a cabinet and searches through it,
Returning with a small, wrapped-up package.

One gift after another, these cycles.
Of course, this one's got its own glow as well.
Inside the package is a small glass tube
And the liquid in there is shining bright.

I know I'm grinning. Just can't help myself.
'You son of a bitch, Fife. This is her blood!
You took some of her blood!' The tube is warm,
And the blood inside is still a fierce white.

He shrugs again, a big gesture on him,
Refuses to meet my eye. 'Yeah. I know
It's not protocol, taking evidence,
But I'd never seen anything like it.

'Something to show the wife and kids, you know.'
The blood is brighter than the bulb above,
Echoing its glow around the kitchen
And amplifying my shadow tenfold.
    'Mind if I hold on to this?' I ask him.
'You're welcome to it. A weight off my mind.
I've got the rest of your stuff with me, too.
You're gonna have to explain something, though.'
    This cycle's beginning to look better
Than the last. He's got my gun, torch, the Heart
model. 'What in the name of Phos is this?'
'That's what a Heart's meant to look like,' I say.
    'Seriously? That small?' He weighs it up.
'About a hundred times bigger, I think.
Don't suppose you've seen a Heart anywhere?'
He shakes his head. 'Sorry.' 'Sure. Worth a try.'
    We sit a while, listen to the clock tick,
Quarter to fourteen, and watch the girl's blood.
There's something hypnotic about its glow:
Something surreal, otherworldly, divine.
    'What now?' asks Fife of me, eventually.
'I find who killed Vivian,' I tell him.
'And what about the Heart?' 'That too, I guess.'
He makes to move. 'You want dropped anywhere?'
    I consider the offer. 'Sure. My place.
I could probably do with some fresh clothes.'
He helps me back into his car, starts up
Drives us back through the city and downtown.

'Phos and fire, Yorke. Your apartment's out here?'
He pulls up next to the sidewalk, takes in
All the dark of the streets and apartments,
Thick like it is out here. Suffocating.

I let myself out, give him some more thanks.
'Sure. Whatever. Good luck. Give me a call
If there's anything you need, all right, Yorke?
Let me know if you find out who did it.'

Fife and his car fade away into Vox,
Leaving me alone and tired and grateful
And, despite everything, despite myself,
Still yearning, still craving Prometheus.

Still wearing Fife's old robe, my things in hand,
I ascend the stairway that takes me home.
I'm fresh out of batteries, but this dark
Is familiar. I know my way up.

Cold feet against cold stone, I skirt glass shards
And discarded needles, discarded ghosts,
Up to my front door. I can hear the hum
Of a radio from down the hallway.

Even outside, I can hear his breathing.
Someone's waiting inside my apartment.
I curse under my breath and draw my gun.
I remember four bullets at last count.

He'll be listening out for the door creaking.
I stand to one side, back against the wall
And push it in, hinges snarling from rust.
His first shot goes wide, through the empty space.

Still, I call out, make it sound like I'm hit,
And then fall silent, close my eyes and wait.
I can hear him moving through the darkness.
Wearing heavy boots was a big mistake.

Never thought I'd appreciate the creak
Of my floorboards, but here I stand, waiting
And forming a mental map of his route
By the way he treads through the apartment.

When he gets close enough, I take a shot,
Hear his own shout, hear his body dropping;
Thump on my floor. I wait for him to die,
Laboured breathing getting shallow, wheezing.

When I'm sure he's dead, I search his pockets,
Find a torch, a knife, a badge and a gun.
Closing the door, I light his torch, see him.
'Shit,' I say. 'Santiago, you bastard.'

Looks like I hit him full on in the chest.
For a while, I'm not quite sure what to do.
Then, I notice the dry blood on his knife,
Near the hilt. 'Fuck you too, Santiago.'

I find some clothes and get dressed, take his coat
And run some water to wash out the stain
Made by the exit wound. It's a nice coat,
Sits comfortable across my tired shoulders.

Son of a bitch saved me some cash, at least.
I don't need to buy some new batteries
For my torch any more. I bin his badge,
Put his gun in a drawer and drag him out.

He's pretty damn heavy for a dead guy.
There's a stack of half-dead ghosts down the hall
And I drop him there. No one will notice.
There's never any lights turned on in here.

My pockets are getting way too heavy,
So I head back for a satchel, load it
And get on my way. Got too much to do
For sleep. Sleep is for the dead, anyway.

Outside, I stride the streets again, past blocks
Drowning in dark, considering Wilson.
I should really go see Dante, but then,
His photo store is on the way. Why not.

> • <

The papers have picked up a new scandal
For the cycle. All progress on the Heart
Is way back on page seven with the sports.
Funny how easy it is to forget.

I guess maybe the news is just too big
For people. It's too much for them to take
That the whole city could go up in smoke
Any time. Smaller news is comforting.

The docks are on strike again like clockwork.
It's a weekly event now. They complain
About a lack of light, a lack of sight,
Tell the rest of us they can't work in dark.

Some politician's been accused of fraud.
As far as I know, they're all in on it,
So this guy must have been pretty stupid
To get caught out: flashing his cash too much.
    Regular news for regular people
More concerned with the weather and themselves,
How bright Joe next door's bulbs are beside mine,
Than the imminent looming doom in Vox.
    But, hell, who am I to be complaining?
Gets me out of the papers, which is great.
Given the choice, I'd be anonymous;
Just another shadow walking the streets.

This time, there's an OPEN sign on his door,
A metal plaque with raised letters hanging
From the mail slot, cold against my fingers.
Still, I'm polite enough to knock three times.
    'Mister Yorke!' A shaft of vertical light
Leaks out as he opens up, smiling wide.
'Real good to see you again, sir. Real good.
I got your note.' He steps aside for me.
    Inside, it's a neat little photo shop:
Tools of the trade scattered round here and there,
Lenses glinting on some work surfaces,
Reflecting the small but warm bulb above.

There's some pictures hanging on the walls, too.
Weddings, portraits, people looking happy
And one of Wilson himself, looking proud.
A small shop for a small but happy man.

'I went and developed your reel straight up,
Soon as I got it. I said to myself,
Must be important if you're on the case.
Saw you all over the papers again!'

'Sure.' I'm more interested in the pictures
Than any conversation with the guy.
'Hope you don't mind,' he says as he grabs them,
'But I had a quick look through. Just to see.'

'Yeah? What's on them?' I take the envelope,
Slide the pictures out, tilt them to the light.
'Truth be told, Mister Yorke, don't have a clue.
I was hoping that you'd know what they are.'

He shuffles around behind me to see.
There's twelve of them total, developed clean.
Looks like Wilson's got a talent for it.
The pictures are clear, but not what they show.

'What in hell's name is that?' I say aloud.
The first eleven show a big network
Of pipes, cables and tiny lights like stars,
Wrapped around a bunch of blackened mirrors.

No matter which way I hold the pictures,
I can't make any sense of what's on them.
It looks like a kind of machine, maybe.
A bit like the set-up in Cancer's vault.

Wilson, the helpful guy that he is, says,
'I had a quick look with a magnifier,
And there's some words printed on the mirrors.
Look. There and there. Like old language, y'see.'

He's right. There are some shapes that look like words
In the old style. I've never seen white ink,
But they're there, white against the black mirrors.
'Can you read them?' 'No, sir. Never learned to.'

The twelfth picture is the most confusing.
I spend a while trying to understand,
But it refuses to make sense to me.
'Any idea?' 'No, sir. Not that one.'

It shows one of the mirrors, but this time
Something's being reflected. A white light
Like a torch, half held over some water,
Against a red and yellow and blue wall.

There's a lot of colour in the picture,
And I can't make sense of the perspective.
'A misprint, maybe?' I say to Wilson.
'Sure could be. It depends on the camera.'

Slotting the pictures in their envelope,
I turn to him. 'How much do I owe you?'
'Nothing at all! Just glad to be of help.
Maybe we could go for a drink some time?'

I head to the door. 'Wilson?' 'Mister Yorke?'
'Thanks for this. But I wasn't here, okay?'
He grins. 'Sure! I get it! But hey, one thing.
Let me know what those pictures mean some time?'

'If I find out, I'll let you know.' I leave,
Back into the black. He watches me go
From the step of his door, waving at me
Until I round a corner, out of sight.
    I know I should be hunting down the Heart,
But... damn you, Vivian. Damn you to hell.
Why do I need to know why you were shot?
Why can't I get you out of my system?
    Dante will have to wait a bit longer.
I'm like a dog chasing a car right now.
Hell if I know why, but I'd keep running
Forever to know why you burn so bright.

> • <

    This time, there's a different face at the door,
Peering defensively over at me.
It's a face that looks weary of weeping
And trying to seem civil. 'Mrs North?'
    'I know you,' she tells me, mumbling the words.
'You're the man from the police who came by.'
I go to remove my hat, remember
I lost it and nod instead. 'That's me, ma'am.'
    'What's happened now? Have you caught him? The man?'
'Caught who, ma'am?' 'The man who did it. Killed her.'
Maybe coming here wasn't a great plan.
'No, ma'am. We're still following up on leads.'

There's a short time in which I realise
I should be explaining myself to her.
'Is your husband in, Mrs North?' I ask.
'Only me. Why are you here, officer?'
  'I was just…' I find myself trailing off,
Glancing down the street at the other homes.
Maybe I should have gone to the Uni'.
Easier than disturbing anyone.

  She sighs, opens the door wide, welcomes me
Back inside her house, bursting with glowing.
I'm caught up in the light, shading my eyes
Against the chandelier, whirls of crystal.

  She looks impatient, waiting. 'Spit it out.'
I'm sure she's appraising me, my bruises,
The way my cheekbones protrude from my face.
'There's something I hoped you'd look at for me.'

  I give her the courtesy of staring
And taking her time to make up her mind
About whether or not to indulge me,
Remembering the last time I was here.

  'Come through,' she says at last, leading me on
Past faceted mirrors, grand old portraits
And shelves full of books, normal and printed.
'We can discuss this in the library.'

  The library is a comfortable place,
Lit warmly by lamps instead of white bulbs.
A fireplace crackles darkly to one side
Among the tall cases, heavy with books.

Mrs North offers me a leather chair
Beside the fire, clears some books from the desk
And pours herself a glass of something dark.
She takes a seat opposite, looking small.

I put the envelope down between us,
Note the way her hands shake as she reaches,
Slides the photos out and glances through them.
She looks fragile, like a cracked piece of glass.

'There's a few words on some of them,' I say,
'In the old style. I was wondering if...'
'If I can read them?' She doesn't look up,
Considering the pictures one by one.

'Where did you get these?' She sips from her glass.
'They're Vivian's, I think.' 'I think so, too.'
At one, Mrs North peers closer, squinting.
'Do you know what it is that she studies?'

'No, ma'am.' Don't know why I never found out.
'She studies Archaeology,' she says,
Present tense again, maybe out of hope.
'And these are pictures of Cancer's ruins.'

Sometimes I wish I'd paid more attention
Back in school, learned a bit more than I did
Instead of skipping classes, chasing girls,
Retaining my ignorance. 'I'm sorry?'

She sighs again, leans back. 'You are sorry.
A sorry lot that could let her be killed.
She was a wonderful girl, officer.
Do I really need to explain Cancer?'

I was never one to be great with words,
Consoling people. 'I'm sorry,' I say,
Like they told us to over and over
During training. I'm sorry. I'm sorry.

But it turns out I really am sorry
And the words come out honest anyway.
Mrs North's face loses its sharp angles,
Softens, its lengthiest shadows fading.

'Cancer, the man, the family, is named
After the Heart. Cancer, the Heart, is named
After the great vessel it once powered.
These are pictures of that vessel's ruins.'

I remember Cancer's speech about boats
That could cross the stars, that our ancestors
Used them to travel here and settle down.
'Where are they? The ruins, I mean. In Vox?'

'No, officer. Quite a way outside Vox.
Past some of the outlying villages.
There's a train, I believe. Are you going?'
Sure looks that way. 'Sounds like a lead to me.'

Maybe there's a crime scene out there somewhere.
The place Vivian's veins were made so bright,
Or a reason why. A bloodstain, bullet
Or some other clue. Any clue at all.

I'm following up on a buried case
With zero backup, barely any leads
And a whole different major case to solve,
And for the life of me I don't know why.

'First, though. The words on the mirrors. Can you…?'
She laughs at me, and it comes out bitter.
'Those? They're not mirrors. They're video screens.
Light-emitting… Oh, what does it matter.'

She takes a closer look through. 'Archaic
Language. Quite a lot that's either nonsense
Or doesn't make sense outside of context.
There are one or two repeated words, though.'

I wish I had some paper and a pen.
My memory will have to do for now.
'Go ahead.' 'You see here?' She points for me.
'It says "conversion" there and "convert" there.'

'Anything else?' 'Not really. Some babble.
That word seems important though, I would say.'
I gather the pictures up, 'Thank you, ma'am,'
Notice there's one still in the envelope.

'Oh.' I drag it out. It's the funny one,
All vivid colour, strange-looking torch light;
An odd reflection caught on a mirror.
'Don't suppose you know what this is?' I ask.

It still looks like it could be a mistake,
The flash of the camera caught reflecting
Colour off a surface. But I suppose
It's worth letting her have a glance at it.

When she looks at it, she begins to laugh,
And this time it's genuine, warm laughter,
Like I've told her a joke. She drains her glass.
'You poor man. Don't you know? Can't you see it?'

And she has to show me, point each bit out.
'You see there? The water? That's an ocean.
And that, behind it? That's a sky and clouds.
And this… this is a star. It's a sunrise.'

> • <

The casino is a lot quieter
At this time in the cycle, dark tables
Made empty by an absence of patrons.
I pass a vacant wheel turning idly.

There's an uneasiness among the staff,
Like I'm a threat to the peace of the place.
I can feel their eyes watching me go by,
Not sure how to deal with me returning.

I'm only here for a passing visit
Before I head to Vox Central Station,
Because Shepherd might be able to help
Solve something for me that no one else can.

His goons are easy to spot, at the bar,
Their fists the size of sledgehammers clenched tight
At my approach, tiny eyes sizing me.
They don't have a single word to greet me.

'Tell Shepherd I need to know what this is.'
I place the bright tube of blood on the bar
Between them, and neither bats an eyelid.
They share a glance, glare at it, then at me.

Shrugging, I turn to walk away. 'Hey, Yorke,
Where did you get this? Doesn't look like Pro'.'
'It's not,' I say to them. 'That's a girl's blood.'
There's a pause, and I turn back to see them.

One has the tube, fingers casting shadows
In thick slabs of dark across the other.
'Bullshit,' he says. 'I've seen a lot of blood
And none of it's ever glowed like this does.'

'Yeah,' I say. 'So, ask Shepherd what it is.
He's meant to be an expert on Pro', right?'
They're staring at me again. 'Right,' says one.
The other pockets the tube. 'Right,' he says.

> • <

The clerks at the bank have their own desk lamps,
One apiece. They look after themselves here.
Even while serving those of us begging
For glows, they warm their hands on points of light.

There's a desk for those who want batteries,
Currency converted into power,
And another for bulbs: strip, bell, white, red.
Get in line, wait an hour, take your pick.

I'm needing cash. Got enough light to last,
And the queue for money is the shortest.
Sure enough, I'm still getting paid wages.
The clerk slips me a hundred past the bars.

I run my fingers across the fresh notes,
Read the raised denominations, embossed
In a way that's meant to be hard to forge.
They all look the same, otherwise: white sheets.

There's a guy selling cigarettes outside
And I grab a pack, join those on the steps
Sucking on smokes, ask one to ignite mine.
There's a contemplative quiet out here.

Most sat out here are staring at the sky.
It's that time in our cycle when our sun
Is visible, or rather, its absence.
On a clear cycle like this, you can see.

There's a black hole moving across the sky,
Taking up space where there should be star-shine,
Like someone's taken a piece of the sky
And painted it black or hollowed it out.

I move along, find a phone booth and call
My department, ask for Dante by name.
He answers, says, 'Shit, Yorke, thought you were dead.'
'Yeah,' I tell him. 'So did I, for a while.'

I let him know I'm headed out of town,
And he's fine with the idea. 'Why not.
You're nothing but a pain in the ass, Yorke.
Keeps you out of my way, out of the case.'

I have to laugh. 'It's nice to know you care.'
'I'm serious, though. This case is screwed-up
And there's people here screwing it up more.
Someone's making sure it doesn't get solved.'

'Yeah… I figured that's why I got that knife.'
Dante shouts at someone in the background
Before speaking to me again. 'Look, Yorke,
You take your trip outta town and stay safe.'

'Sure. Thanks, Dante.' 'Fuck you for getting stabbed,
Though. Now I have to face this mess alone.'
'You're not alone.' 'Sure as hell feels like it.
Let me know when you're back in town, okay?'

'Right.' I go to hang up, but he stops me.
'One more thing. If you see Santiago,
Tell him to get his ass back here right now.
Nobody's seen him since yestercycle.'

From where I am, I can see our dark sun,
Our hole in the sky. I can see it pass,
Swallowing starlight as it travels by.
'Sure,' I say to Dante. 'I'll let him know.'

> • <

Vox Central Station is a mess of noise.
Engines thumping, steam hissing, shrill whistles,
The sounds of the crowds and the distorted
Crackling announcements over all of it.

Spread out from the dark, arched central hallway,
Lit by a single flickering dull bulb,
A dozen hallways filter travellers
Towards platforms and trains. Away from Vox.

The place I'm headed to is called Manus.
One of those villages far out from Vox,
Receiving little or no energy
From our three Hearts. They live in a deep dark.

I push through crowds of people, commuters,
Vacationers and visitors and friends,
Carrying heavy luggage, bags filled up
With pieces of their lives, destinations.

I follow ridges set into a wall
Down one hall, taking me to a platform,
And after a while in the dark, there's light
In the form of a bright railroad headlamp.

The platform is packed with people shouting,
Waving tickets, conductors ushering,
Bodies pushing and vying for some space:
A kind of chaotic mess of boarding.

And beyond them all squats the train, darkly.
It's an enormous black engine, belching
Steam from its great chimney, whistle howling,
Empty coaches inviting company.

I wait my time, watch for an opening
In the crowds, enough space to move on board
Through those trying to escape the city,
But without the means to afford tickets.

Without the trains, there's no other way out.
A car, you run out of fuel pretty quick.
Walking, and you're lost in a few cycles.
The rails keep other settlements tethered.

I spot a gap and push past a couple
Embracing, hand my ticket to the guard
And get let on board, up the metal steps
And through to a mostly empty carriage.

There's an empty booth and I take a seat,
Shutting the door behind. There's a window,
Which make these carriages fairly ancient.
I ignite a smoke, watch the platform move.

I see the faces of those left behind,
And from here they look like they're fading stars,
Small round points of glowing vanishing fast
And turning dark as the train powers on.

There are no lamps set in the carriages,
But there's enough light being reflected
From the powerful lamp guiding our way,
Set into the front engine, to give sight.

I sit back, smoke another cigarette
And barely notice as we exit Vox.
There's no difference in dark, unless you look
For it, turning from close, walled in, to vast.

> • <

I think I forgot how to sleep normal.
The clacking rhythm of the train lulls me,
Makes me drowsy, watching the dull flashing
Shadows cast by telegraph poles outside.

There's nothing else to see. Only shadows
And the glinting reflections cast in drops
Of rain as they trail down the window glass,
Streaking long pale lines as they slowly drag.

    I've been left alone in my closed-off booth,
And the train seems to be mostly empty.
I see no one pass through the corridor,
Only vague human shapes shifting at stops.

    And as we get further away from Vox,
There's more time passing between every stop
Until it feels like I've always been here,
Hungry, and bruised, and tired. So very tired.

    I close my eyes, and when I open them
There's a guy sitting opposite, reading
A book and ignoring the rain outside.
Another moment lost, and he's vanished.

    The rain stops and starts again just as quick.
I must be drifting away between blinks,
But no amount of sleep is curing me
Of the ache that goes right down to my bones.

    More time passes and my hunger gets bad
Enough that I leave my seat, search for food.
The rocking corridor is nearly black,
Lit by the meagre glow from the windows.

    There's someone else stood at the other end
And for a fleeting moment I glimpse her,
Caught in the flash of the train's bright headlamp
Reflecting from a surface in the dark.

'Rachel?' I rub the sleep from my tired eyes
And stumble down the distance in between,
To the end door, dividing coach from coach,
And by the time I get there she's long gone.

The next coach is empty, as is the next,
And when I reach the dining coach at last,
I'm questioning myself and what I saw.
Some half-dreamed figment in the dark, maybe.

I order a tall glass of something strong
And a dish that doesn't sound revolting,
Take a seat to one corner and admire
The low glow of the bulb warming this coach.

There's a scattering of others in here.
Tired-looking travellers eating cold meals,
Nursing half-drained glasses and cigarettes,
And avoiding each other's hollow eyes.

The whisky is weak and way overpriced,
And my meal tastes like trash, but I'm surprised
By how grateful I am to have them both.
Hell, I even go back for a dessert.

I ask the guy at the bar how long left
Before Manus and he shrugs, checks his watch,
Pours me another glass and drains his own.
We don't talk, but we do drink, and that's fine.

My eyes keep wandering towards the door,
Like I'm expecting Rachel to walk in,
And I wonder about her, who she is,
Why she takes up so much space in my thoughts.

The drink eventually takes hold of me
And my hand finds its way back to my throat.
What I'd give for a shot of Pro' right now.
Something to take the edge off the cycle.

The train shudders onwards, ever onwards,
Cutting a line through the black with its lamp,
And even hundreds of kilometres
From Vox, I can't escape the dark in me.

I'm the only one stepping off the train
And onto the lonely wooden platform.
Beyond the train's headlamp, I'm confronted
By a vast, unfamiliar darkness.

The conductor's kind enough to ask me
If I'm sure this is where I want to be.
The middle of nowhere. A nothing place.
Even the stars have abandoned me here.

I watch the train until I can't see it,
And then I'm immersed in the emptiness
And, for the first time in what must be years,
Feeling some discomfort in the darkness.

I close my eyes and try to hear my way,
But it's no use. I don't know where I am.
There's just the wind, and the baleful howling
Of something wild way off in the distance.

Santiago's torch has some life left
And it's been better looked after than mine.
By it, I find my way to a dirt road
And tread the tracks, on the way to Manus.

I pull my coat close, intimidated
By the limitless black to either side.
There are no buildings out here for the torch
To find; no comforting closeness of walls.

There's a fence, and I stop to shine the torch
Into the field there, watch the waving grass
And the flabby blind white cows as they graze,
Calling out, softly, to one another.

They're a pleasant sight, and I watch them move,
Rubbing up against each other, soft flesh
Meeting soft flesh, content in their small field.
Content to live not knowing what light is.

Further along the track lies the village,
A rough collection of wooden buildings
Looking fragile, like they might blow over
In a strong breeze; like they're made of paper.

There's noise coming from what looks like a church,
So I pocket the torch and step inside,
Join the congregation of mourning folk
Dressed in black and gathered round a statue.

Their idol of Phos is carved out of wood,
And while not as bright as the one in Vox,
There's still something shining behind His head,
Extending His lengthy jagged shadow.

I'm expecting a coffin, someone dead,
But there's no such thing. Beneath Phos's feet
Is an ugly-looking piece of blown glass,
Blackened around the edges, slightly cracked.

'You're new in town?' says a guy, approaching.
He's speaking softly so no one's disturbed.
'What's happening?' I ask him, whispering.
With a gesture, he leads me back outside.

He's short, round like he's eaten a few meals,
Wisps of grey hair uncoiling in the wind.
The sign of Phos is pinned to his jacket.
'I'm Pastor Michael. You're from the city?'

'Sure am,' I say. 'What's going on in there?'
His eyes don't meet mine. They rest on my scar.
'We're a simple folk out here, sir,' he says.
'We mourn the loss of our best filament.'

I suppose I really should have figured.
They mustn't get too much light in Manus,
So far removed from Vox, it's an event
When a bulb dies. No easy replacement.

'I'm sorry, sir, I didn't catch your name?'
Michael's suspicious, which is fair enough.
Guess they don't get too many visitors.
'Detective Inspector Yorke,' I tell him.

'Welcome to my village, Inspector Yorke.
Welcome. But, if you don't mind me asking,
What brings you all the way out to Manus?'
I ignite a cigarette and inhale.

I explain I'm here to look at the wreck,
The ruins of Cancer, and he reacts,
Says, 'I thought we were done with all of that?'
Over the wail of someone from inside.

'All of what?' 'Listen. We're a quiet lot.
We just want to be left alone, all right?
Can't you understand that?' I shake my head.
'You're gonna have to bring me up to speed.'

'So you're not with the University?'
'I'm not.' He takes a while to weigh me up,
Caught in the slender strip of leaking light
From a crack in the door of the small church.

He sighs, at last. 'Got a spare cigarette?'
'You smoke?' 'Not very often, inspector.'
Leaning his head, he lets me ignite his,
White smoke drifting from between his fingers.

'They came a few months back. A noisy crowd
Of students and academics, big cars
And bright lights, unloaded from the railroad,
Disturbing the cattle and crushing crops.

'It took them another three months to leave,
And we're still repairing the mess they made.
Of course they threw round plenty of money,
But the people here don't care much for that.'

'What were they doing?' I ask. 'I'm not sure.
Something to do with the ruins, I think.'
'It sounds like a kind of expedition.'
'I'd say so, but I didn't ask questions.'

Vivian must have arrived with that team,
Which would explain her photos well enough.
'I need to see the ruins,' I tell him.
'But you still haven't told me why you're here.'

I stamp the stub of my cigarette out.
'There's been a murder,' I say, 'a young girl,'
And as I do, people start streaming out,
Their service complete, and Michael moves off.

'I'll take you there,' he tells me, 'in a while,'
And starts shaking hands, offering comfort.
People stare or glare at me as they leave,
Like I'm here to smash bulbs and scare cattle.

I take the time to ignite a new smoke
And watch them huddle, vanish in the dark.
Leaning back against the church, I wonder
Again about the colourful photo.

It's occupied my thoughts for a while now:
That reflection I still can't make sense of.
I realise, leaning there, a big part
Of why I came here is to look for it.

Maybe up close I'll be able to see
Properly what it is, what Mrs North
Called a sun rising. I know part of me
Wants to find the reflection, prove her wrong,

But I think that I want her to be right.
I want there to be a place where the sun
Can make a sky blue, an ocean sparkle.
Where a sun can rise, and be made of light.

> • <

When I was young, my father would take us
On trips outside the city, to visit
My grandparents where they lived, in the dark
Outskirts of one of the coastal port towns.

We'd skim flat stones across the black ocean,
Eat by the light of my grandfather's lamp,
That singular, yellowed, ancient beacon,
And listen to him telling his stories.

He'd tell us about lighter times in Vox,
When batteries and bulbs were plentiful
And houses had windows because the streets
Were all lit up by the brightest street lamps.

He'd tell us about the time Taurus failed,
Vox's fourth Heart drained of its great power
All at once one cycle, core turning black
And ruining the Taurus family.

He'd tell us about faraway places;
Cities where red lights are hailed as lucky,
Entire countries living in total dark,
Types of insects with tails that hum and glow.

You could see the love in my father's face,
His appreciation for his parents,
For my grandfather's experiences;
His ability to tell a tall tale.

I hated every moment being there,
Repelled by the suffocating darkness
They always seemed comfortable living in.
I never understood their happiness.

❯ • ❮

Pastor Michael drives in total darkness,
His car rattling, shaking and jarring me
As it meets potholes in the earthen track.
I have to brace myself to keep stable.

❯ • ❮

Pastor Michael lights an ancient lantern
That looks like it's been made out of pieces
Of a dozen different lanterns, repaired
So many times it's been turned to patchwork.
      'You're gonna have to be careful,' he says,
Guiding me the rest of the way on foot
Along a muddy track between gnarled trees,
All snarls of branches trying to snag me.
      'The wreck's half sunk into the bog,' he says,
Stepping careful over a fallen log
And helping me across it with a hand.
My boots are starting to fill with water.

'When they came, they cleared the track out, but now
It looks like the swamp's nearly reclaimed it.
There's a damn good reason the salvage teams
Tend to avoid Cancer: too dangerous.'

The trees get closer as we get deeper,
Wading through smaller pools of still water,
White leaves glinting moisture, the sky covered,
Until the track is difficult to find.

Still, the pastor knows his way well enough,
Helping me over the worst of the tracks
And before too long, he tells us we're here,
That we're at the ruins: Cancer's ruins.

There's nothing obvious that I can see.
I was expecting a big jagged shape,
Maybe something resembling a huge boat
Resting on a shore, but there's nothing here.

Michael has to show me, lantern swinging,
The wide entrance like a cave, half buried
In mud and grown over by trees and vines.
'I can wait, if you like,' he says to me.

I tell him that it's a good idea
And offer him a cigarette in thanks.
He takes it and holds it protectively,
Like it might grow legs and run off somehow.

I light Santiago's borrowed torch
And nearly trip over a thick cable
Snaking into the wreck by the entrance.
It looks new. 'What's that?' I ask the pastor.

Michael shrugs. 'Power line from the railroad?
I remember they were having trouble
Getting it stable. Power comes and goes
In Manus. Probably the same out here.'
　　'It gives me something to follow, at least.'
'Sure. Try not to take too long, inspector.'
I nod my thanks and, ducking my head low,
I head inside, tailing the black cable.

　　The corridor I head down is a mess
Of rust, dripping, busted pipes and thick mud.
It's hard to make out what this place looked like
Before it was a half-buried ruin.

　　The cable winds steadily on, deeper,
Through narrow hallways and wider spaces,
Past collapsed ceilings where roots have pushed through,
Heavy locked metal doors and flooded rooms.

　　The stench of the place is overwhelming,
Earthen and rusted and rotten at once,
And every few steps I disturb something,
Cause the place to creak and groan eerily.

　　Being here gives me the creeps, I admit.
It feels cold, and I have to keep stopping
To make certain it's only me in here
Trying to find what was being powered.

　　The way the torch reflects sets me on edge,
Glinting off water and light surfaces
And casting weird shadows at odd angles,
Making me confused, lost and uncertain.

Despite my wariness, I get a sense
Of the place as I go. It is a boat
By the way it feels, all heavy sealed doors,
Low-hanging metal pipes and compact rooms.

I still have little sense of the boat's scale,
Beyond the fact that it must be massive.
It's at least twice the size of the biggest
Shipping tanker that I can remember.

Hard to believe how ancient this place is,
That it could ever have travelled the stars.
I guess it could just be another boat.
Cancer might have been spinning me a tale.

I realise that without the cable,
I would be completely lost in the wreck.
Each room looks the same as the last: a damp
Collapse of parts and the swamp's incursion.

Yet, as I travel deeper in the dark,
The ruins begin to get less ruined,
Like I'm heading towards some untouched core,
As of yet free of the bog's influence.

I turn a corner, following a twist
In the cable's trail and take a wrong step,
Throwing me off-balance. Then, I'm falling,
Sliding in the dark down a muddy slope.

The torch follows me, whirling round madly
And throwing my panicked shadow about
Before crashing against something, crunching
And fading out, leaving me in the black.

I slide and roll, gathering fresh bruises,
For what feels like a near eternity,
And eventually come to a hard stop,
Slammed against a metal wall, jarring me.

I take a moment to breathe and calm down,
But my blood's thumping noisily in me
And there's a pain in my leg that won't fade.
Slowly, I manage to sit up, take stock.

The torch is gone. I'm lost, without a glow.
On the other hand, my leg's not broken,
Just twisted and bruised, causing needling pain.
And, above everything else, I'm not dead.

I have to laugh. Mostly for damn Cancer,
Who seemed pretty convinced that I'm lucky.
If anything, the past few cycles seem
To be solid proof of the opposite.

Here I am again, alone in the dark.
No ghosts here, no match heads, nothing at all.
Just good old Inspector Yorke, following
Up on a case he was meant to forget.

It's one of those cycles that's just so bad
You have to laugh. It has to be a joke.
Phos must be up there somewhere, tears rolling
Down His star face in mirth at my fortune.

At least I've still got some cigarettes left.
I ignite one, inhale deep, feel my blood
Begin to die down at last. I can hear
The sounds of the wreck again, so quiet.

Among them, there's a sudden whirring noise
And a small doorway becomes apparent,
Lit up by some glow on the other side.
I stop laughing at last and try to stand.

It's not much of a walk. I stumble through
To a room that seems to sparkle brightly.
The cigarette drops from my open mouth,
Made forgotten. It's a hell of a sight.

Tiny lights flicker, like they're uncertain
Of themselves, and between them, dark mirrors
Seem to glow, black but still emitting light.
This... is the place. The place in the photos.

I don't know how the lights work. They're tiny
Bulbs, smaller than my finger, and they glow
Brighter than any I've known back in Vox.
More confusing still are the black mirrors.

There are words written on them, unstable
And scrolling up, and they look almost like
They're writing themselves. I press my fingers
Against the glass and wish I could read them.

There's a steady humming as I move round,
Studying the mirrors and tiny bulbs,
Trying to figure out what I should do.
I understand none of what's happening.

Searching around in my muddied satchel,
I dig the envelope out, slide pictures
And try and compare them with the mirrors.
Some of the same words are there. 'Conversion'.

And it's that same word, over and over.
'Conversion', and 'convert', scrolling upwards,
Being written by whatever machine
It is controlling the lights and mirrors.

I move on through the busy and wide room
And there, like a dream, like it's a mirage
Is the mirror reflecting or glowing
The image like no other. And by Phos…

It's flickering steadily, unstable,
And I can't look away, can't comprehend
The way the sparkling water is moving.
And it is moving. The image… it moves.

The sky in the image is red, blue, white,
And so is the water, so is the sea,
And in that sky the clouds are drifting white
In swirls like smoke, trailing lazy, aimless.

And there are some dark shapes whirling around
That might be bats but bigger and broader,
And there's a yacht in the sea with white sails,
Billowing massive in the gusting winds.

The image is on a six-second loop
And I realise I've memorised it,
Staring wide-eyed, wide-mouthed at the moment
Captured in the mirror and repeating.

And now I know Cancer wasn't lying,
That this boat did sail the stars from a place
Where light comes easy, where all is so bright,
Because right there is an alien sun.

I press my fingers to the glass, trying
To feel the bright warmth of that fierce beacon,
That brilliant moment captured in time,
That sun. That bright sun. That bright sun rising.

And as I do, just like I flicked a switch,
The power fails and everything goes dark.
The humming stops. The lights and mirrors die.
But I haven't forgotten what I saw.

How could I forget that moving image?
It's scarred into me now, I can feel it,
Just like I can feel the scar at my neck.
In the dark, I wait, and I remember.

Even though I still can't breathe, and there's blood
Streaming down from my neck where the rope caught,
I find the strength to stand and grab the gun
Where he left it, lying on the table.

And when he walks back in from the bathroom,
He just stops there and folds his hands neatly,
Doesn't say anything, standing, waiting,
Watching me with no expression at all.

Then, when I shoot him, he doesn't call out.
He takes it like I've done him a favour,
Like I'm being polite, shaking his hand,
And it feels like nothing. Nothing at all.

FIFTH CYCLE

I lose track of how long I spend sat there,
Listening to the steady dripping echoes
Coming from some leak in a pipe nearby.
Guess I'm waiting for the lights to come back.

As if I could stay here with the mirrors
And watch that image repeat forever.
Six seconds. All I want is one more glimpse,
But it doesn't come. The mirrors stay dark.

I stay for as long as I feel I can,
Until my hunger is a needling pain
And my fingers have turned numb in the cold.
Only then, I move and seek the cable.

My fingers trail the machines, metal, glass
And the tiny bulbous nubs of dark bulbs,
Dead without the power from the railroad.
We took Cancer's Heart a long time ago.

Soon, I realise that I'm lost again.
The walls are thick with piping and cables
And I'm directionless, lost in the wreck,
Getting slowly hungrier and colder.

I encounter a door that feels different,
Sealed with a wheel instead of a handle,
And smaller. Possibly a kind of hatch.
I figure, what the hell. Might be a way.

Gripping tightly onto the rusted wheel,
I heave it, feeling how weak I've become,
How my wasted muscles are protesting,
And the acute sharpness of my hunger.

The wheel is fixed. It refuses to turn,
Locked in place by five hundred years of rust.
I slump down against the door, giving up,
Wondering if this place will be my tomb.

And, of all things, my thoughts turn to Rachel;
That moment back on the train, glimpsing her,
Imagining her there, following me,
And there's a fraction of something bright there.

Like my thoughts of Rachel are a fraction
Of the wonder I felt for that image,
But constant, like she's a fraction of light,
A lone star in the black sky of my thoughts.

So I stand again and kick the damn wheel,
Because I guess there is light, after all;
Some small points of light in my existence,
And they're enough to keep this corpse going.

Groaning, resisting, the wheel starts to turn
As I kick it, balancing on the leg
Still hurt by my fall. But then, I'm all hurt;
I'm running out of places to be bruised.

Something clanks noisily inside the door,
Some aeons-old lock sliding back for me,
And the door begins to creak heavily,
Swinging towards me and leaking water.

I can hear it, feel it lapping at me
And filling the hall fast as it rushes,
Threatening to bowl me clean off my feet.
I grab hold of the wheel to stay upright.

Just my luck. The hatch opens to the bog.
The icy water reaches my shoulders,
And then, before I can take a deep breath,
I'm completely immersed and freezing cold.

I've got no choice and barely enough air
In my lungs to last long in the water.
I kick out, beyond the hatch in the black,
And try to work out which way is upwards.

Better to drown than starve, I'm supposing
As I push with my weary arms and legs,
And I can't feel them any more. In fact,
All I feel is the burning in my lungs.

I realise that the wreck is ruined,
That I've flooded it, that no one will see
That moving image that I saw in there.
But I remember. I'll never forget.

Just as I'm close to giving up, too cold,
Too tired, and out of air, and out of time,
There's a light above me, like a dull star,
Made rippling by the surface of the bog.

I kick towards it, desperate to taste air,
Grabbing at the water with my cold hands
And watching bubbles rise up from my mouth,
Chasing that light with the last of my strength.

And there's a hand dividing the water,
Reaching for me, taking hold of my hand
And tugging me towards that dull beacon,
Beyond the grip of the swamp, to the air.

He drags me onto solid ground, gasping,
Setting the lamp down on a fallen log
And helping me to sit up against it.
'Inspector!' It's Michael. 'Are you okay?'

Throwing water up and choking, laughing,
I grab the man by the wrist. 'I'm not dead.
It's a joke. A joke. Phos won't let me die.'
I lose consciousness at last. Still alive.

> • <

'You're as tough as old boots, Virgil,' she says,
In that way she does, with a scarlet smile,
And she takes my hand. 'Like leather,' she says.
I notice how small her hand is in mine.

> • <

I wake to the sound of rain drumming loud
On the roof that must be there above me.
I'm in a bed again, comfortable, warm,
But dark. Nothing like Cancer's offering.

There's a little light illuminating
The wooden floor, seeping under the door,
And by it I can see some empty frames,
Bits of furniture, the feet of statues.

I swing myself and stand, still unsteady.
He must have undressed me, found me a shirt
And pants to sleep in, dry after the swamp
Nearly claimed me, drowned me in a deep pool.

In the next room, I find Pastor Michael,
Humming to himself and working a lathe
By the light of his lantern. It's a mess
Of wood shavings, warmth and pleasant noises.

He glances at me over his glasses
But doesn't stop. 'Welcome back, inspector!'
I find a chair that looks halfway finished,
But it doesn't give way. 'You made all this?'

'Phos has a way of giving us each gifts.
I like to think I've got a way with wood.'
He finishes with the lathe, turns to me.
'You, I think, are lucky. Very lucky.'

'People keep telling me that,' I tell him.
'By all means, you should be dead, inspector.
I've seen your bruises, and the needle marks,
And the place you've been stabbed. Why aren't you dead?'

I shrug as he boils a kettle for me
Over the fireplace, brewing some coffee
And making me a thick sandwich to eat.
'You nearly drowned,' he tells me, like it's news.

The coffee causes me to shake, shudder
With its strength, but I feel the heat fill me,
And I'm surprised by how hungry I am,
Savouring the sandwich like it's my last.

'Why are you out here, inspector? Really?'
I'm sure I told him. 'There's been a murder.'
'But why you? You should be in hospital.
Surely someone else can investigate?'

'Because,' I tell him, 'there's nobody else.'
And it all comes out. 'Nobody else cares.
They can forget that a girl was murdered,
But I can't. I need to find who did it.'

The pastor watches me finish eating,
Removes his square spectacles and cleans them.
'And did you find what you were looking for?'
'Looking for?' 'In the ruins. Cancer's wreck.'

'Yeah… I did find what I was looking for.
But it doesn't give me any new leads.
It's a dead end. I shouldn't have come here.
I'd be more useful back in Vox, I think.'

'Well…' He sighs. 'Maybe there weren't any leads
Because they took them, cleaned up, when they left.
I watched them go, and their cars were heavy,
Trucks filled with bulky, covered instruments.'

'You mean they took something from the ruins?'
'I mean, it looked like they left with a lot
More than they arrived with. At least, I think.'
I finish up. 'That's pretty helpful. Thanks.'

'No problem. Only, do me a favour?'
Michael moves around, searching his carvings.
'Sure.' 'Don't go pushing your luck, inspector.
Phos can be fickle. Enjoy His favour.'

He returns with a carven mark of Phos,
And I realise the church's statue
Was made by the same guy. Pastor Michael.
'For you,' he says. 'May Phos shine upon you.'

'Thanks, Michael.' 'No problem. There's a train soon.
I'll drive you down to the platform, okay?'
'Okay.' He hands me my clothes, clean and fresh,
And goes back to his work, carving idols.

The sign of Phos is small, fits in my palm,
Hardly weighs a thing. When I'm fully dressed,
I grab some cash from my coat and leave it
On the dresser, kept in place by the sign.

❯ • ❮

I watch Pastor Michael's silhouette fade
And dissolve into the dark as I go,
Another booth to myself on the train,
Content to be left alone: room to think.

I look through the contents of my satchel.
The Heart replica survived well enough,
And I take my gun apart to dry it,
But Vivian's photos are a damp mess.

They're a mush of unsalvageable pulp
And I throw the whole damn heap in the trash.
The last evidence that a bright sun rose
Now lies with Wilson, with the negatives.

> • <

It's a relief to step down from the train
And join the milling crowds in the station,
Back in the familiar dark of Vox,
Immersed in the closeness of my city.

I slip past families reuniting,
Lost tourists and commuters pushing through.
I shake my head to clear it of the sleep
Still clinging on and clouding my judgement.

There's a troupe of sharp businessmen queuing
To have their shoes shined, eyes following me
And glinting, reflecting the train's headlamp.
They look predatory, like I'm their prey.

A couple of guards are clearing some ghosts
From the front of the train, aiming truncheons
And bruising spindly limbs, forcing them back
From the tracks, some caught underfoot, trampled.

On from a chauffeur holding a red torch,
Flashing it as a signal for someone,
I spy the exit tunnel and push through,
Past a guy loudly selling cigarettes.

I can't help but smile, caught up in the stink
And sounds of my city, its deep shadows
And tall walls, endless multitude of folk
Going about their complex, networked lives.

On the edge of leaving the train behind,
I glimpse a pair of eyes I recognise,
Turning to meet mine before vanishing
Among the tight crowds trying to exit.

Only a moment, but I'm sure I saw
Rachel there. I call her name and push through,
But it's difficult, the tunnel turned dark,
People cursing as I shoulder past them.

Emerging into the central hallway,
I wonder if I'm going mad, dreaming
I'm glimpsing Rachel wherever I go.
Standing on my toes, I can't make her out.

The bulb here is dull, dusty, pretty weak
And any of those shifting silhouettes
Could be her, streaming from the main exit,
Beneath that tall black arch, between the gates.

Still, I rush through, trying to find her there
Among the people scattering like bats
From a cave, dispersing into the streets,
Catching cabs or retreating in the dark.

Turning on the spot, studying faces,
There's nobody I recognise. Strangers
Surround me, ignoring me, streaming on,
Ignorant to my plight, my questioning.

I shake my head again, try to clear it.
Maybe I've finally snapped, given in
To the pressure being applied to me.
Frankly, I'm surprised that it took this long.

A shining, glinting car among the cabs
Swings round to where I'm standing, near the road,
And from it emerge my two favourite goons,
Unfolding like the car's too small for them.

'Boss wants a word,' says one, laying a hand
Firmly on my shoulder and steering me
Towards the car. 'About fucking time, Yorke,'
Says the other, 'we've been waiting for hours.'

They bundle me roughly into the back
And pull out, drive into the city, south.
The car's comfortable enough, I suppose,
And my two friends grumble to each other.

I have to ask them, 'Do you guys have names?'
'Sure,' says one, 'Franklyn. This is Montana.'
'Shut the fuck up, Franklyn,' says the other,
Steering a corner, heading deep downtown.

The streets begin to get busy with cars
And Montana curses, joins the traffic.
'More fucking strikes,' he growls, hands off the wheel.
'Fucking docks. Where the fuck have you been, Yorke?'
I shrug. 'Out of town.' 'Yeah, we guessed that much.
You'd better have a fucking good reason.
I'm sick of sitting in this fucking car.'
He slams one meaty hand down on the horn.

'Sorry about Montana, he's just tired,'
Says Franklyn. 'You shut the fuck up, Franklyn.'
Outside, we can see people flashing lights,
Holding the traffic up with their protests.

Everyone looks tired and irritated:
The protesters, other drivers and folk
Trying to walk by. Nobody's happy.
It's a well of unrest in the city.

'You hungry, Yorke?' asks Franklyn. 'I'm hungry.'
'For fuck's sake, Franklyn. What does this look like?
A fucking nursery?' 'But we've got food?'
Montana sighs. 'Fine. Let's have a picnic.'

The three of us eat some cold pie and watch
The traffic move by, slow as a cripple.
'What does Shepherd want?' I ask Montana.
'Hell if I know. Not our place to question.'

Eventually, the traffic starts moving
And Montana steers us down a dark street,
Headlight illuminating stacks of crates
And weather-beaten storage: warehouses.

They park up among a few other cars,
Shining new like this one, all in a line
Beside a dark warehouse, droplets sparkling
And glinting on each from the recent rains.

Stepping out, I can hear and smell the sea,
The crashing of waves, and the scent of salt,
And the chirping of whirling fishing bats.
I'm led across, to a guarded entrance.

Ducking in, Franklyn and Montana lead
Me up a set of creaking wooden steps
And into a dark office, lit up low
By the solemn glow of a fake candle.

'Can't you afford a real one?' I ask him,
Shepherd, the anonymous shape sat there
In the shadows behind the single desk.
He chuckles. 'Good to see you, Mister Yorke.'

I'm pressed roughly into a wooden chair.
'My guys say you've been out of the city,'
He tells me. 'You've been missing all the fun.'
'Yeah?' The fake candle flickers, on a loop.

'I've been waiting for you,' he says to me.
'Thought you'd like to be around to see it.'
'See what?' 'Well, Mister Yorke, I found the source.
The source of the money, and where it went.'

Sounds like Shepherd's been following some leads
Of his own. 'Who paid for the Heart, you mean?'
'Correct, my good friend. Would you care to guess?'
'No. But I think I know who received it.'

'Go ahead.' 'You were right about the cops.
I had one try and kill me twice this week.'
'And yet you're still here.' 'Yeah. I shot him dead.'
'Bravo, Mister Yorke! You do have a spine.'

'So, tell me. If the police took the Heart,
Then who paid for it? Who has the money?'
Shepherd, ever one for drama, pauses,
Still chuckling to himself. 'It was Cancer.'

I can't tell if it's meant to be a joke.
I lean back in the chair, watch the shadows
Dance by the light of the ersatz candle,
But it makes no sense in my head. 'Cancer?'

'That's right. Cancer. They used his own money.'
'Who?' 'Allow me to explain, Mister Yorke.
Mister Cancer, being the man he is,
Set a scholarship trust up some years back.

'You know. To help students out at Uni'.
It took a while for my men to figure
Out what was happening, but it's all there.
That trust has been emptied for the Heart theft.'

'By who?' 'That, I'm not sure of. But, I know
How they did it, and where the money went.
It was pretty clever, I must admit.
Took them years to pull off, to take it all.

'The money from Cancer's trust has been used
By students, but students that don't exist.
The money was funnelled to an account,
One single account, until it was used.'

'Whose account?' 'Anonymous, I'm afraid.
Whoever did it was very careful,
But not careful enough, because I traced
The money and who got paid for the job.'

'The police?' 'Sure. But mostly, just one guy.
Again, would you care to place a wager?'
I weigh up the few potential suspects,
And come to a quick conclusion. 'Garfield?'

Shepherd claps and chuckles to himself. 'Yes!
Right again, Mister Yorke. It was Garfield.
The man who went and organised the theft
Is the same man investigating it.'

Figures. There was something wrong from the start
About the chief, the way he spoke to me
And dealt with Cancer, all calm, collected,
Like he knew something that we all didn't.

'He can't have stolen it alone,' I say,
And Shepherd agrees. 'Of course not. But then,
Now's your chance to ask him who else did it.'
'What do you mean?' 'Follow me, Mister Yorke.'

Shepherd stands, and for the first time I see
His face. I can't help but stare at the scar
There, wrinkled up in a river of flesh,
Burned into one side of his heavy face.

He catches my eye and turns serious.
'You might be asking why I trust you, Yorke.
And this,' he points to his red scar, 'is why.
Vox has put its mark on us both, my friend.'

Franklyn opens the door, and I follow,
Head full of thoughts vying for attention.
I'm dreading what's going to happen next,
Because I can guess what Shepherd has done.

And there, wrapped up almost like he's a gift
And hanging upside down from the ceiling
Over a black pool of water, Garfield
Swings idly, conscious, gagged and looking scared.

'For you,' smiles Shepherd. The room is a dock,
Wide and walled, private, with a gaping hole
Leading out to the dark ocean beyond.
Franklyn holds a bare bulb, plugged in somewhere.

It's a hell of a scene, every shadow
Made massive and moving by the bright bulb,
The black water reflecting and waving
And Garfield above it all, swinging slow.

I realise I have an audience.
The dock is full of Shepherd's paid heavies,
Lolling on crates and watching proceedings,
Dark shapes among dark shapes in the background.

Montana tugs the gag from Garfield's mouth
And the chief starts coughing and spluttering.
'Get me down from here! Yorke? Is that you there?
Arrest these men! What are you waiting for?'

I realise I'm angry. 'Was it you?
Did you send Santiago to kill me?'
He falls silent, and that's enough for me
To know the truth. Shepherd got the right man.

'Who paid you?' I ask him, and I notice
His gold tooth has been torn out. He's a mess,
Bruised and shaken by whatever they did
To get him down here, strung up like fresh meat.

   He doesn't reply until Shepherd says,
'Answer the man, Garfield. We have your wife.'
And even then he takes his time, weeping,
Salty tears meeting the salt of the sea.

   'Someone from the Uni', I think. Some man.
We never met, instructions by phone call.
I only worked out he's from the Uni'
Because he let slip about his student.'

   'His student?' 'Yeah. You know. The bright-veins girl.'
'Vivian?' 'Sure. Whatever. He told me
To bury the case, she was a problem,
Called her "one of my students" and that's it.'

   Well, I'll be damned. Maybe I should have known
The two cases were linked. It all leads back
To the University. All of it.
Vivian, the Heart, all because of them.

   'Thanks,' I tell Garfield, and then Shepherd, 'Thanks.'
'That's enough?' says Shepherd. 'Yeah. That's enough.'
Except it's not, but I don't realise
That I still had a question quick enough.

   Shepherd draws his gun, a shining pistol
That looks more like an ornament, and shoots
Chief Garfield clean through the top of his skull,
Blowing his brains into the black ocean.

'Sink him,' says Shepherd, idly motioning,
And they lower Garfield into the sea,
Weighed down by rocks and still leaking crimson
As he goes, vanishing quick and easy.
  'His wife?' I ask Shepherd. 'Already dead.'
He shrugs. 'Anyway. I still have to ask.
Where have you been, Mister Yorke? We missed you.
My men say you caught a train to Manus.'
  The way he can keep talking, casual,
Like he hasn't just committed murder
In front of an officer of the law
Sets me off balance. It's hard to react.
  'Yeah,' I tell him, dazed by Garfield's murder.
'Out of town. Manus. To see the ruins.'
'Which ruins?' 'Cancer's wreck. The boat, I mean.'
'Ah,' he says. 'And did you find anything?'
  'Not much. But I did find that the Uni'
Was out there a while back, excavating,
Taking stuff from the boat and back to Vox.'
'That's interesting,' says Shepherd. 'Yes indeed.'
  'What now?' I ask, as he holsters his gun
Idly, like he didn't just kill a man.
'Go and find the Heart, Mister Yorke,' he says.
'Right,' I say. Then, 'Right,' again. Shepherd laughs.
  'Franklyn, Montana, drive him where he wants.'
The scarred man strides away, still laughing loud,
And I don't know if he's laughing at me
Or Garfield, or the whole damn mess of it.

'Shepherd!' I call after him, remember
I left him Vivian's blood to look at.
'The blood?' 'It's blood,' he calls back. 'Is that all?'
'That's all, Mister Yorke. Blood that glows brightly.'
　'Time to go, Yorke.' Franklyn steers me away
From the dock and back out, into the rain.
It hits me at once in a chill of drops
And wakes me from my dazed kind of stupor.
　I'm cursing at myself for not asking
Garfield about any accomplices,
Those officers guilty of helping him
Steal the Heart and kill all of Cancer's guards.
　I'm pushed back into Montana's car
And he starts the engine, lights the headlight,
Illuminating the wall of mild rain
Spattering the dark sea front endlessly.
　'Where to?' asks Montana, backing the car
And turning back out into the city.
Ahead, the protesters are still going,
Chanting their bleak mantra. 'Give us some light.'

❯ ● ❮

　There's something important I need to do.
I step out of the car, into the rain,
Hands deep in pockets, ducking my head low
And striding between the drops down the street.

It's a quiet district, not too wealthy,
But made visible by those few store fronts
That make enough to afford a front light:
Often flickering, but a pleasant sight.

The street is mostly empty, which is fine.
I need some space to think, to consider
All the information I have so far
And what I should be doing about it.

I know this sidewalk well, intimately,
Because I grew up here. I know the road,
The curve of the flagstones and every crack
Along them, rain flowing down in rivers.

The stores have changed, but the street never will:
Dents in the thick brick masonry, the way
The light falls out of the old grocery
Door, the only one left with a window.

I come to my destination and stop,
Rain dripping down my face, soaking my boots,
Because my father's hat store hasn't changed.
I know those shadows, the depth of each one.

I'm hesitant because it's been two years,
And I had no plans to ever come back,
But I can't think of anywhere better
For what I need. I take a breath, step in.

The bell's the same, that half-broken tinkling
Heralding my entrance. I wipe my boots
Out of habit, dripping on the carpet
And taking a look around at the hats.

There's a humble bulb buzzing at the back,
Set to flash on when a customer comes,
And it reveals the shadow of Lewis,
My father's apprentice, as he steps out.
    'Virgil? Do my eyes deceive me?' he smiles.
I always had a soft spot for the man,
The same age as me and destined to be
The one to take my father's small business.
    'Lewis.' I shake his hand. 'I need a hat.'
He's a happy, warm guy, proudly shows me
Around, is patient with me. I notice
The tough skin on his fingers, the prick marks.
    I find the kind I'm looking for, broad brimmed,
The style my father was in demand for.
Lewis makes a few adjustments for me.
'How have you been, Virgil? It's been a while.'
    'Alive,' I tell him, 'and keeping busy.'
'Of course. But…' and he leaves that word to hang,
That unspoken question, and the reason
I didn't want to come back here again.
    'There,' he says, eventually, and hands me
The hat. It's a snug fit, comfortable, wide
Enough so I can hide my eyes, my scar.
I thank him, but he won't accept money.
    I make to leave, open the door, dull bulb
Blinking black automatically. 'Virgil?'
Comes his voice, out from the dark. 'Where were you?'
And I find myself paralysed by him.

I can't answer because I don't know how.
How is it right? That a man can not show
For his own wife's funeral? It's not right,
And I still can't explain it. I don't know.
　　Summoning enough strength, I walk away,
Let the door close behind me, bow my head
And lose myself down the dark street. 'Virgil?'
I hear the door, his voice calling for me.

＞•＜

Dante looks like he's been to hell and back,
Got a table to himself at a wall
And keeping a tight hold of his coffee
Like he's been drowning and it's a lifebelt.
　　'Yorke,' he says, nods, motions for me to sit.
The diner's mostly empty, vacant seats
All in a row along the lengthy bar,
Bored-looking waitresses standing idly.
　　'You got my message?' I sit opposite.
'Yeah. Things have gone to hell back at HQ.
Garfield's gone missing, and so has his wife,
And there's still no sign of the fucking Heart.'
　　I order a coffee as black as black
And sit back, remove my hat, admire it.
'I think I know who has the Heart,' I say.
Dante squints, shakes his head looking at me.

'What the fuck happened to you, Yorke?' he asks.
'It's been a funny cycle,' I tell him.
The coffee arrives and it's way too hot,
But I drink it anyway, feel the burn.

   'All right,' says Dante. 'Who has the damn Heart?'
'The same guy who killed Vivian,' I say.
Dante drains his coffee, gives me the look
He saves for unpredictable suspects.

   'I'm serious,' I tell him, find the Heart
Replica and put it on the table.
He takes it, rolls it around in his hands
And recognises it. 'Norton?' he says.

   'Yeah. You remember that interview, right?'
'The one you fucked up?' 'Yeah, that one. You see,
I think he was nervous about something,
Something bigger than Vivian, maybe.'

   Dante sighs, leans back, drops the replica.
'What makes you think that?' 'Something he mumbled.
Look. I've been out of town, at Cancer's wreck.'
'Cancer's wreck?' 'Yeah. The place the Heart came from.'

   'You're losing me.' 'All right. I'll be simple.
There's a word that keeps coming up, you see.
"Conversion". Something to do with the Heart.
And the only guy I've heard saying it—'

   '—is Norton. Yeah. I remember,' he says.
'So what's it meant to mean? This "Conversion"?'
I shrug. 'No idea. But there's a guy
Who might. Knows all about Hearts. Magnusson.'

Ordering a second coffee, I wait
For Dante to process my theory.
He plays with the Heart replica, turns it,
Chewing at his bottom lip thoughtfully.

For a while, I'd considered telling him
About Santiago, about Garfield,
But this way is easier. He's honest,
Too honest maybe, and I'd rather lie.

'Not bad, Yorke,' he says, after a small while.
'Better than any leads I've had so far.
It's a long shot, but hell, I'll come along.'
I breathe a sigh of relief, drain my cup.

'You bring a car?' I ask him, grab my coat.
He slides out. 'Of course I fucking well did.'
Outside, the rain's finally subsided,
Leaving a gleaming sidewalk in its wake.

Dante unlocks the squad car he borrowed
And starts it up, engine turning, growling.
We follow its headlight through the city,
Igniting cigarettes, wisping white smoke.

> • <

The University is real busy,
A hive of students swarming around us.
There's a kind of close tension in the air,
Like everyone knows something that we don't.

Dante doesn't seem to feel it, strides on
Down the hall like there's no one else in it,
Shouldering through without apologies.
I'm caught up in his wake: bruised arms, sharp looks.

I take the time to try and listen in,
Catch snatches of idle conversation,
But kids shut up when I'm close, like they know
I'm an outsider here: an intruder.

The reception is busy with students,
But Dante doesn't let the press stop him,
Happy enough to push bodies aside
And knock noisily on the wooden desk.

I can't spot Rachel. Maybe she's not in.
They're all strangers behind the reception.
I hang back, let Dante do the talking.
The excitement in the air puzzles me.

But, like in a dream, like I summoned her
With my thoughts of her, Rachel then appears.
She looks radiant, and I'm stuttering,
Surprised by her sudden glowing presence.

'Virgil,' she says, holding on to papers.
'What brings you back to the Uni' again?'
I take a breath, glance around at the kids
Laughing, joking, caught in some excitement.

'Did you catch a train?' I say, studying
Her face, the dance of the shadows on it
As she frowns. 'I'm sorry?' 'A train,' I say.
'I don't—' I shake my head. 'Doesn't matter.'

Guess it was in my imagination,
After all. I dismiss the memories.
'What's all the excitement about?' I ask.
She looks around. 'Last cycle of the term.'

She's probably right, but for some reason
It doesn't fit right in my head, seems off,
Like I'm still missing something. But she says,
'Meet me tomorrow,' and I can't think straight.

There's that smile again, slow as a sunrise,
But not the dark star that we orbit here:
The rise of that alien sun I saw.
A bright emergence of warm brilliance.

'Tomorrow?' 'Yes. Come and meet me,' she says.
I glance about and Dante's still busy.
There's nobody around listening to us.
'Sure. All right,' I say, and the words feel light.

'East Park. Do you know it?' 'Sure, yeah I do.'
'Okay. Around ten o'clock sound all right?'
It does, and I let her know that it does.
'I need to go now, but I'll see you then.'

She leaves, and I watch her go, heels clicking
Across the stone floor, between bright glowing
Patches where the white bulbs above reflect.
Too bright for me; I need to keep squinting.

And when she's gone, has vanished entirely
Among the turbulent crowds of students,
Dante grabs me by the arm. 'Come on, Yorke.
Magnusson is in. We're gonna talk now.'

> • <

The lecture theatre is bright, noisy
And brimming with moving bodies, fighting
For space among the seats with each other:
Students carrying heavy bags of notes.

Doctor Magnusson ascends towards us,
Up the steps dividing the room in two,
Checking his pocket-watch as he climbs up,
Like he's got somewhere important to be.

Mostly, I'm impressed by the chandelier.
It's like the one the Norths have, but bigger;
So many curls of crystal hanging up
It looks like they've captured stars in the glass.

Students pass us, streaming to find seating,
Jostling around us. Magnusson looks pleased,
Like we've come here to give him an award.
'Gentlemen,' he says, without a stutter.

I take a moment to make sure it's him,
And it definitely looks like the man,
But not the same terrified, stuttering
Doctor who came to talk about the Heart.

'I'm afraid I have a lecture starting,'
He tells us from the step below, and yet
He appears taller than we are, somehow.
'Tell me, how can I be of assistance?'

Dante looks to me and raises a brow
As if to tell me to do the talking.
I clear my throat. 'You know about Hearts, right?'
'Yes,' he says. 'I know a lot about them.'

'There's a word that keeps coming up, you see.
We were hoping that you could explain it.'
Magnusson glances at his watch again.
'Certainly. Which word, pray tell?' '"Conversion".'

And it's like I've spoken a magic word.
The doctor's face becomes cheerful. He claps,
Says, 'Wonderful!' and then, 'Please, take a seat.
I'll have the class explain it all for you.'

Magnusson turns, hopping from step to step
Away from us, towards his tall lectern.
I exchange a confused glance with Dante,
But neither of us go after the man.

Instead, we do as we're told, finding seats
At the back, the closest to the shadows.
I keep my hat on and so does Dante,
Like we're afraid the bright lights might burn us.

'What do you reckon?' I ask of Dante,
And he doesn't say much to me, just shrugs,
Settles back in his seat. 'Hell if I know.'
I lean forwards, wait for it to begin.

Magnusson stands up behind his lectern
And addresses his quiet audience.
I could have sworn he was smaller, fragile;
On the verge of breaking into pieces.

'Class,' he calls, 'we have some guests this cycle.
As such, we won't be discussing matter.
Instead, we'll be going back to basics.
Our guests need to know about Conversion.

    'Who,' he goes on, 'can tell me what it is?'
Maybe a hundred hands raise in the air,
Like they're reaching for the lights up above,
Grasping for the stars in the chandelier.

    'You there,' points Magnusson to a student.
The boy in question stands, says, 'Conversion
Is a change from one state to another.'
'Very good. Now. Conversion Theory?'

    A new student is pointed out, stands up.
'Conversion Theory states that matter
Can be changed into light and back again,
Provided that the light is engineered.'

    'Superb. The practical applications?'
'Varying,' says the next student, standing,
'But, according to ancient principles,
Conversion lets us travel between stars.'

    'So!' says Magnusson, somewhat delighted,
'What you're saying is that our ancestors
Travelled seemingly endless distances
By, effectively, turning into light?'

    'Sort of,' says a quiet voice near the front.
The doctor stops, smiling even wider,
And turns towards it. 'Ah! Dear Benedict.
Please, tell us all what you mean by "sort of".'

All eyes turn to the student who spoke up:
A small guy with a quiet voice, who says,
'Well. That's putting it simply. It's more like…
It's not really a Conversion, you see.'

'No? Then what is it?' 'It's a… destruction.
From what I've read, Conversion Theory
Requires three different stages in order
For it to work properly. Three stages.'

'Brilliant, Benedict. And what are they?'
'Destruction, Transit and Reconstruction.'
'Correct. Can you explain them for the class?'
'I can try.' 'Take your time,' says Magnusson.

Benedict pauses and gathers his thoughts,
Then says, 'Destruction. The original
Item, be it a person or vessel,
Is deconstructed into code. Data.

'That data is kept in the form of light,
A kind of programmable meta-light,
Which knows to reconstruct at its End Point.
As such, the original is no more.

'But the data, the light, can then travel.
That's stage two. Transit. One small flash of light.
That burst from the Conversion Point travels
In every direction across the stars.

'Only when a part of that burst of light
Reaches its pre-programmed destination
Does stage three occur. That's Reconstruction.
A copy of the vessel is then made.

'But that's what I meant, sir. It's a copy.
"Conversion" makes it sound like the vessel
Beams across the universe on a wave,'
There's some chuckling, 'but that's just not quite right.'

'Very clever, Benedict. Be careful,
However. While our ancestors struggled
With the philosophy of Conversion,
Our place this cycle is somewhat simpler.

'Our guests are only wanting a quick brief
On what Conversion is. A summary
Would suit our needs perfectly. Anyone?'
Magnusson sweeps his hand across the room.

One or two hands rise up hesitantly,
But not enough to satisfy the man.
He returns to his lectern, leans on it
And looks up to where we're sat, at the back.

'I think we had it at the beginning,'
He says, almost softly, just loud enough.
'Conversion means light. A beautiful thing.
Turning something or someone into light.'

> • <

'Did you get any of that?' asks Dante.
The theatre is emptying slowly,
Students clumped together and discussing
The class. They shuffle past us, where we sit.

I shrug. 'Some of it. The important parts.
Like how it's possible to turn someone
Into light. Reminds me of Vivian,
Or something close, maybe. Could explain her.'

'Sure.' Dante's eyes are narrowed and glaring
At Magnusson as he gathers his things
At the front of the hall, still smiling wide.
Looks like Dante has something on his mind.

'What are you thinking?' Dante shakes his head.
'He reminds me of… you know those suspects
Who reckon they can't be caught? That they've won?
That they're better, much smarter, than we are?'

I've seen my fair share of those through the years,
And I'm surprised that I hadn't noticed,
But Dante's right. It's like he's done some crime
He thinks we can't catch him for; that he's safe.

'I fucking hate people who think like that,'
Dante mutters. I lean back, look around.
The theatre's mostly emptied out now,
The last student's footfalls echoing loud.

'What are we gonna do, then?' asks Dante.
'Catch the bastard.' 'Magnusson?' 'Both of them.
Magnusson, Norton and whoever else
Happens to be involved. Are you with me?'

Dante lifts a cigarette to his lips
And strikes a match, igniting it. 'Hell yeah.
I don't care who he's killed or what he stole;
I want to wipe that smug look off his face.'

I wonder, then, why it took me so long
To get Dante involved. He's like a dog
Who's caught a scent; a better cop than me,
And I'm sure glad to have him on my side.

'Excuse me!' calls Magnusson as he steps
Up to meet us, 'I'm sorry, you can't smoke.
There's no smoking in lecture theatres.'
Dante makes no move to put his smoke out.

I stand. 'Interesting lecture, Magnusson.'
Irritated, but still smiling, he nods.
'I hope that everything was clear enough.
It can be a tricky subject at first.'

I figure we're past the point of lying
And come right out with, 'Where's the Heart, doctor?'
And without skipping a beat, he replies,
Says, 'I'd be happy to take you to it.'

There's a short pause as each of us takes stock
Of the exchange, broken when Dante says,
'And Norton?' 'Certainly. He's there as well.'
Magnusson wrinkles his nose at the smoke.

I figure he's in the mood to confess,
And try, 'What about Vivian, doctor?'
He frowns, says, 'Who—' before realising,
Then says, 'Ah. The girl. Yes, I can explain.'

Dante smoothly draws out a pen, paper,
And is poised to take some notes. 'Go ahead.'
The doctor smiles thinly at him, as if
The cigarette is some kind of insult.

'Gentlemen. I am happy to explain,
But not here. Let me take you to the Heart.
I have a car and I can drive us there.
It's not far, I promise. Not far at all.'

I exchange a glance with Dante, who shrugs.
Looks like it's up to me. I weigh the odds,
And while I'm certain it'll be a trap,
I'm way too curious to turn him down.

And hell, both Dante and I have weapons,
We can look after ourselves. Magnusson
Doesn't look like he'd be much of a threat.
I know it's foolish, but still I'm nodding.

'Why not. Lead the way, doctor,' I tell him,
And he strides up through the doors, expecting
Us to follow, through bright shining hallways
And back out, into the dark parking lot.

'I hope you know what you're doing, Virgil,'
Mutters Dante to me as we follow.
'Me too,' I tell him, fingering my gun
And feeling the cold weight of it. 'Me too.'

> • <

I keep my hand on my gun while he drives.
Dante's in the back, one hand on his seat,
Ready if he tries to do anything:
Drive us off a bridge or onto some tracks.

I've been so desperate to find some answers,
It's taken me this long to realise
We should have just cuffed him, made him direct
Us wherever we're going. Too late now.

The temperature's dropped significantly.
I can see my breath, and outside there's frost
Sparkling in the car's single white headlight.
I hold my coat closed to keep the warmth in.

Magnusson has his watch on the dashboard
And keeps glancing at it, seconds ticking.
'Got some place important to be?' I ask,
But he shakes his head. 'Just keeping an eye.'

He's driving us away from central Vox
And out towards the suburbs, the outskirts,
Through darker districts and slum-like buildings.
We pass less cars as we go, less headlights.

Eventually, it's just us on the road,
The single point of illumination
Along the mostly empty roads and streets,
Skittering slowly across frozen ground.

There are some shapes moving around out there,
Lost-looking wire-frame figures following
The light of our car, shivering pale ghosts
Huddling together in the sudden cold.

There's a hell of a lot of them out here,
Near the edges of Vox, where there's no light:
The remnants of light-addicted people
Turned mad and frail by their own poverty.

'Do you know how many there are in Vox?'
Asks Magnusson, steering us through the slums.
We pass what looks like a whole family
Of ghosts huddled together to keep warm.

'Ghosts?' I watch their eyes glinting hungrily,
That glint fading as we round a corner.
'A few hundred?' Magnusson takes us on
Past the ruins of old buildings collapsed.

'Wrong. Two per cent of the population.'
The slums start to give way to the country,
And we leave Vox, and its ghosts, behind us,
Traded for long fences and foliage.

'No. That can't be right,' I tell Magnusson.
'That would mean… thousands.' 'Hundreds of thousands.'
He doesn't say more than that, turns quiet,
Lets that statistic sink in; all those ghosts.

The headlight illuminates some cattle,
Standing in groups for warmth, like Vox's ghosts,
Breath steaming from their quivering nostrils,
Hooves stamping against the cold, frozen earth.

I realise he's taking us way out
Of Vox, and a sudden sense of panic
Fills me, that we might get lost on the way.
'Just where are you taking us, Magnusson?'

The man himself isn't wearing too much,
Just a jacket, but he's not shivering.
Smiling, glancing at the time, he drives on,
Confident through the dark of the country.

'Not much further,' he claims, tapping the watch,
And I'm beginning to regret coming.
We should have just stayed and interviewed him,
Applied some pressure and got some answers.

Dante's starting to get restless as well,
Shifting his weight in the back and smoking
Another cigarette, uncomfortable
With being this far out from the city.

There's a flash I assume is the headlight,
And for a moment the country around
Is lit up, all frosted and sparkling white.
Magnusson lets out a cry of laughter.

He slows the car to a crawl and then stops.
'Something's wrong with the engine,' he tells us,
Stepping out into the cold open air
And pulling open the engine cover.

'I don't like this,' growls Dante, as a flash
Of light illuminates the white country
For the second time, the low, cloudy sky
And the solid glinting grasses below.

I realise it can't be the headlight
Causing the flashes: they're too bright, too big.
I open the car's door and step outside
With Dante, looking around for the source.

We're on a road somewhere way out of Vox,
And there's nothing to see except cold fields,
But what's important is that we can see
Those fields even though the headlight is off.

I have to blink as there's another flash,
Like someone's lit up the whole world at once
With some massive lamp. We can see the sky,
And silhouetted against it is Vox.

There's a crunch and a clank from the engine
And Magnusson throws something to the ground
That looks important. He then faces us,
Hands coated in oil, grinning in triumph.

'What have you done?' I'm turning on the spot,
But I can't work out what's happening here.
I draw my gun, point it at Magnusson,
Who raises his black hands. 'What have you done?'

'The engine's broken. We'll have to walk back.'
This time, the flash doesn't stop, the light stays,
And it feels like I can see forever,
Such vast distances; the world filled with light.

'There's something wrong with the sky,' says Dante,
And, panicked, I look up. He's right. The sky
Is all wrong. It's white, and behind the clouds
Is a vast beacon, our sun, glowing bright.

Magnusson says nothing. It starts to snow,
And it feels like I'm frozen in one place,
Staring at the sun, our dark sun, so bright,
Unable to think or react. Staring.

❯ • ❮

'Why?' I ask, stood on the tips of my toes,
Trying to buy some time for me, for her.
He looks at me. 'You all ask that question.
Why does it matter? You're about to die.'
　　'Because it's got to mean something,' I choke.
'Fine.' He sighs. 'Because nothing changes here.
Because people live out their lives content,
While the city around them gets darker.
　　'Because I am a force of change in Vox.'
'You're insane,' I tell him, struggling to breathe.
'Possibly. Probably. But am I wrong?'
In one quick motion, he kicks my chair out.

SIXTH CYCLE

The snow has turned the gun cold, my hand numb,
But still I keep it aimed at Magnusson,
Trying to comprehend the bright above;
Our dark star turned light behind those white clouds.

'It was Norton's vision,' says the doctor,
'Which is why I brought you both way out here,
To give him some time to enjoy the sun
Before you go and throw him somewhere dark.

'He'll be up at the Observatory,
Watching the sky, maybe with some students.
We have our students to thank for their help,
Recovering some of Cancer's machines.'

My teeth are chattering, I'm shivering
And I pull my coat closer, staring up,
Unable to tear my eyes from the sky,
From that bright bulb hanging behind the white.

'Conversion takes a tremendous amount
Of power, which is why we took the Heart.
It was the only way to make it work.
We launched it a few cycles back, out here.'

And as he says that, I'm remembering
That moment before I got stabbed, that flare
Rising in the sky that wasn't a flare
But a rocket flying towards the sun.

'It's only temporary,' he tells us,
'It won't last for more than a few short hours,
Until the Heart is completely empty,
And there will be a few small side-effects.

'The temperature, for one. It will be cold.
Certain kinds of radiation, as well.
But nothing with any lasting effect.
We calculated no long-term damage.

'I suppose I should apologise, too,
For coming in and misleading you both.
The Heart was always in capable hands.
We felt it necessary to buy time.'

I can hear Dante behind me, mumbling
And it sounds like a prayer of thanks to Phos.
The snow is rushing down fast, covering
The road and the car, smothering in white.

'Isn't it beautiful?' says Magnusson,
And he's stood strong against the snow, smiling,
Oily hands still black from his sabotage.
In that moment, I hate him. I *hate* him.

'How many people did you kill?' I ask.
'What?' My question seems to confuse the man.
I'm no longer looking up at the sky.
My eyes are fixed on him, on his black hands.

'How many?' I shout, waving the cold gun.
'I-I don't know.' His stutter has returned.
'But it-it was necessary. For this.'
'For change?' 'Y-yes… Don't you… c-can't you see?'

I can hear Dante, and he's stopped praying.
'How many, Dante?' He stands beside me,
Glancing from me, to the gun, to the man:
The small man with black hands stood in the snow.

'Twenty-five guards,' says Dante. 'Twenty-five.'
Magnusson is beginning to shiver.
He pulls his jacket close, snow coating it
And repeats himself: 'All necessary.'

And despite the cold, despite the bright sun,
All I'm feeling is a bitter anger,
The terrible rage I've been ignoring
For two years, surging up again in me.

Because I know this guy. I know his type:
Using people's lives as a currency
To be traded in for some insane goal.
Sure, the sun is bright, but people are dead.

There's something that I'm still needing to know.
'What about Vivian?' I ask the man.
'You can arrest me now,' he says to us,
But I don't move. 'What about Vivian?'

'L-look… she was going to reveal it,
What we were doing. I— We had no choice.'
I can feel my trigger finger tighten.
'What did you do to her?' I shout at him.

He takes a step back, tracking through the snow,
Scared of me now, his confidence all gone.
Dante's put a warning hand on my arm,
Muttering at me to calm the hell down.

'I-it was a test. To see if it worked,
To see if the old machine could still run.
And… and it didn't quite work. We both thought
She'd be made into light. But… only part…'

'Her blood? You only converted her blood?'
'Y-yes… the equipment… was still faulty…'
'And she was *still alive*?' 'Y-yes… so I…'
'You did what?' 'I… shot her… I… I had to…'

'Fuck you!' I pull the trigger, shoot him dead.
His body thumps into the snow, bleeding,
Running red in rivers along the white,
And I stride across, shoot him two more times.

'Fuck you!' I'm still pulling the gun's trigger,
Clicking on empty, when Dante steps in.
'For fuck's sake, Yorke, he's dead! Put the gun down!'
And he has to drag me back by the arm.

Still, in my head I'm shooting Magnusson,
Unloading bullets into his body,
Releasing all the rage I've kept pent up
For years, killing him over and over.

> • ‹

It takes a long while for the rage to leave,
Dissipating slow, like my steaming breath.
I watch it rise among the flakes of snow,
Joining the mass of white smothering all.

The sun continues glowing bright above,
The victim of Norton's experiment,
And I feel the need to keep watching it,
Like it might vanish away if I don't.

I've never seen everything look so white.
The fields, the car, Dante as he shuffles;
All white beneath the white sky, the white sun.
The only black is Vox's silhouette.

Even now, out here, the city looks dark.
It's a collection of tall rectangles
Gathered on the horizon in a heap,
Like someone's piled up a bunch of boxes.

I lift my numb fingers, catch a snowflake
And admire the way it glitters in light,
The light of a bright sun, and I wonder
About what it's like back in the city.

I imagine it's a kind of chaos;
Rejoicing in the streets, bulbs being smashed,
Noisy Phos worship and hysteria.
Nobody's told them it's temporary.

Without my surging, fiery hatred
Filling me, the snow is taking my heat,
Making me weak and numb inside and out.
I'm dazed, tired, surprised at my own actions.

The doctor's body is slowly freezing,
Turning to ice in the snow; turning white.
The gun's still on the ground and half buried.
If we stay here, we'll be buried as well.

Dante's doing something to the engine,
But the car's refusing to get going.
He slams the hood shut and curses at it.
'Bastard cut the fuel line. I can't fix it.'

The snow begins to slow, white clouds heaving
The last of their contents on the white world.
Dante stamps across, helps me to my feet.
'You all right to walk, Virgil?' he asks me.

I nod, weary, drained, but able to walk.
We trudge down the road, towards the city,
Leaving long tracks in the snow, in our wake,
All the way back to the car, the body.

'How many cigarettes have you got left?'
'I count eight, but only seven matches.'
'I've got four, but a fresh book of matches.'
'You reckon they'll be enough?' 'Sure, I guess.'

> • <

We run out of cigarettes pretty fast,
Taking our time with the very last pair,
Sat on a fence, watching the clouds roll by
And the sun glowing coldly behind them.

'He was right, you know. It is beautiful.'
I don't disagree, squinting up at it.
It's probably the finest thing I've seen,
But I don't feel anything. Only numb.

We take a short-cut through a grassy field,
Boots crunching swathes through the snow in long streaks,
The unseeing eyes of cattle glinting
Across at a nearby wooden shelter.

The most confusing thing is the distance.
I've never been able to see this far
All at once, and it keeps surprising me
How big the world is and how small we are.

I feel insignificant beneath stars,
But right now I feel even less than that,
And I find myself longing for shadows;
For a place to hide myself from the light.

The lack of shadows makes me feel nervous.
I keep wondering where they're all hiding,
Where all that dark I know so well has gone,
Like it's hidden, buried beneath the snow.

I've never seen my own shadow so small
And so pale, following hesitantly
As if it might vanish among the white
Overpowering everything out here.

Vox doesn't seem to get any closer.
Those looming silhouettes in the distance
Only seem to get taller as we go,
And I wonder just how far up they go.

Some cycles, when the sky is clear, stars out,
You can get a sense of Vox's towers
From the space they darken, scratching at stars,
But from here they look infinitely tall.

Without any cigarettes, I'm restless,
Trudging, irritated through the long field,
Climbing over gates and through more paddocks.
I'm trusting Dante's sense of direction.

The only thing that's keeping me going
Is Dante, resolute against the snow,
Silently ploughing on, eyes to the sky
And lips moving, saying a prayer to Phos.

There's a look on his face I've seen before,
A few cycles back, at the cathedral.
Dante is in awe of the sky, the sun.
I am humbled by his humility.

He takes my hand, helps me over a fence,
And I'm wishing I knew what it was like
To feel anything except hot anger
Or this endless, freezing cold hollowness.

We reach the edge of land and I stumble,
Dante holding me back from the cliff-side.
I wasn't expecting the drop to come,
The sudden view, going on forever.

We have, unwittingly, come to the sea,
And there it is before us, endless white
Reflecting the white sky and the white sun,
And I can't see where the sky meets the sea.

Dante braces himself against the winds
And stares into the white, admiring it
While I cower behind him, panicking
And trying to slow my quickened breathing.

I work up enough courage to join him,
And there, hands in pockets, we watch the sea.
For the first time, I match some sounds to sights:
The crashing, spraying waves meeting the shore.

I would gladly collapse before that view,
Fall to my knees and watch the white ocean
Until the sun's brightness begins to fade,
Except for Dante, who turns to me, says,

'Come on then, Yorke. Not much further to go.'
There's a new emotion etched on his face,
Something close to a smile, but genuine,
Like the man's had one of his prayers answered.

And I follow, more in awe of Dante
Than the sky. In awe of my only friend.
The only guy who's put up with my shit
These past two years without any complaints.

We travel carefully along the cliff,
Keeping to the coast and watching bats fly,
Fluttering, confused in the open air,
Black dots sweeping around against the white.

More fences block our way, but we cross them,
Grumbling about the lack of cigarettes
And all the usual noise between us:
The news, the city and all the darkness.

    And as we get closer to the city,
Close enough to see the shape of the quay
And the boats there, none sailing this cycle,
I say to Dante, 'Hey, wait a minute.'

    He doesn't stop, just turns to me, scowling,
'Get a move on, Yorke. We've got shit to do.'
'Wait. Dante. What if I paid for your kids?'
'What the fuck are you talking about, Yorke?'

    I don't know why I never thought of it,
Something so obvious. 'The Uni' fees.
You can't afford them, right? Well. Let me help.
I've got a whole bunch of money saved up.'

    Dante keeps walking. He doesn't react,
Doesn't reply for nearly ten minutes.
Before he does, he lets out a long sigh,
Like he's breathing out all the dark in him.

    Then, he says, 'Why would you do that, Virgil?'
I shrug. 'I'm not using any of it.'
'I'd pay you back. It'd be on a loan.'
'Sure,' I tell him. 'But you won't be paying.'

    He stops at last, turns to me, glowering,
His coat billowing out, dark in the snow.
'What do you mean?' 'I won't take your money.
We can make your kids pay me back after.'

And I've never seen Dante laugh this way
Before, like it's heaving out from his ribs.
He shakes his head at me and turns away,
Keeps on walking towards the dark city.

'You're a piece of work, Virgil. You know that?
A piece of work.' He glares out at the sea.
'Phos and fire, I'd kill for something to smoke.'
I follow behind, eyes to the white sun.

We hit the suburbs without much trouble,
But Vox, central Vox, still looks far away.
Despite the collapsed ruins of houses,
It doesn't feel like we're in the city.

We walk right down the centre of the street,
Tracing the planted glinting reflectors
Because there's nobody driving out here.
In fact, there's nobody out here at all.

I was expecting chaos, riots, noise,
But there's nothing and nobody to see.
The streets are still and there's a calm quiet,
Like the settled snow's muffled all the sounds.

The twittering of bats echoes around
As they flutter between collapsed buildings,
Spiralling around an open church spire
Snagging at the white clouds drifting above.

'Where is everybody?' I ask Dante,
But he doesn't reply, steps round a car
Left in the middle of the street, coated
In a light layer of half-melted snow.

    The snow is beginning to melt at last
As the temperature rises, the sun's warmth
Returning to some degree. I wonder
If the clouds will go, if we'll see the sky.

    As the houses get closer together,
Becoming detached and semi-detached,
The lack of people starts to worry me.
I wonder if they're all inside, frightened.

    Heck, I wonder if they've noticed at all.
There's no windows in these houses, designed
To keep the light in and away from ghosts.
Could be they're all still inside with their bulbs.

    We cross some invisible division
In the streets and enter the slums at once,
Confronted by the filth and the squalor
All too obvious in the bright white light.

    There's still no movement, no people to see,
Not even a ghost wandering these streets.
Only dirty flaps of canvas, old bricks
And steel drums where they light their fires for warmth.

    I stop for a moment to catch my breath.
We've been walking for what must be hours now,
And I'm pretty exhausted, need a smoke,
Something to eat: those base human urges.

Dante's kind enough to wait a small while,
Rubbing his hands together to warm them
And glancing at the empty cloth houses,
Empty of their wasted ghost residents.

'Where do you reckon they've all gone?' I ask.
Dante shrugs. 'I don't know. What would you do?
If you were a ghost and you got that sun?
All your prayers answered at once. I'd go mad.'

I glance up again, make sure the sky's white,
Relieved to see that the sun's still glowing.
I'm not sure how much longer it'll last,
And I realise I don't want it gone.

We've wasted near half the cycle walking,
Exactly as Magnusson had planned it,
Buying time for Norton to enjoy it.
I shake my feet to get blood back in them.

What's keeping me walking is the knowing
That we need to find and arrest Norton.
That he can't win; get away with murder,
Even for the sake of that bright white sun.

We carry on past tumbled-down buildings,
Entering a nice district, no people,
Gates abandoned, street lamps still glowing dull,
But Vox feels like it's getting close at last.

Its tall towers are taking up some sky
Instead of just lining the horizon.
It won't take us much longer to reach them,
Maybe find out where everybody's gone.

Dante spots some cigarettes in a car
And wastes no time in breaking the window,
Grabbing the pack and igniting a smoke.
'Hell,' he says, 'nobody around to see.'

We smoke in silence and round a corner,
Come to one of the five bridges in Vox,
All crossing the city's unseen river,
And at last we find some people, sitting.

There's a few cars scattered across the bridge,
Engines off, doors open, drivers absent.
Those people on the bridge are at the edge,
Sat and watching the sky; watching the sun.

It's a tranquil scene, and we pass them by,
Stepping carefully around smiling folk,
Muttering softly to one another,
Mesmerised by all that light in the sky.

I take the time to look at the river,
Seeing it properly for the first time,
And it's disgusting: a brown flowing sludge
Dragging all of Vox's filth to the sea.

On the other side of the bridge, there's more
People sat around, looking at the sea,
Caught up in the calm claiming the city.
Some of them greet us as we pass. 'Hey there.'

For a while, as we go, I'm enchanted
By the way the city's stopped, eyes turned up,
And it's a struggle to not watch with them,
To stop, find a patch of sidewalk, and look.

But I begin to notice some people,
Various folks, different shapes and sizes,
Still striding the streets about their business,
Glaring, irritated, at those who've stopped.

They're a minority, but still a sign
That the sun won't solve all of our problems.
That it won't fix the city, its people.
That, as I suspected, it just won't last.

People are always talking about change,
But the truth is, nothing ever changes.
You can turn our dark sun bright, but people
Will still be people: stupid, demanding.

You can turn our dark sun bright, but people,
Some people, will carry on with their jobs.
Give it a week and you would never know
This even happened. People never change.

We enter the city proper, the streets
Coiling around towering apartments
So tall that the sky becomes some white lines:
Those spaces in between the tower blocks.

There's less light from the sky reaching these roads
And there aren't many watching, some walking,
But most just going about their cycles
Like nothing's happened. Like the streets are dark.

Dante looks like he wants to shake people,
Tell them to wake the fuck up and notice
The sun, but I know better than he does.
I carry on and try to ignore them.

> • <

Water runs down the Observatory
As the last patches of snow melt away.
It's getting warmer out by the minute.
The clouds above are starting to look thin.

I'm wondering what kind of sky is there
Behind them, so far remaining hidden.
I wonder if it'll be like the sky
In the picture: reds, yellows, oranges.

This place is annexed onto the Uni',
But out of the way, in an open space
Where its glass dome has vision of the sky
In all its glory; space to see the stars.

We're directed there by happy students,
Sitting around on benches and laughing,
Proud of their work. We pass and we don't laugh.
Dante looks like he'd rather arrest them.

But there's only one guy that we're here for.
Professor Norton, the visionary;
The man with the idea strong enough
To have men murder each other for light.

It's a hell of a light, I give him that,
Fills up the whole sky, the entire city,
But I keep going back to Vivian
And the fact that she's not here to see it.

The door's open. Looks like we're expected.
Dante nods, ignites one more cigarette
And makes sure he has his handcuffs ready.
'No shooting anybody this time, Yorke.'

It's not like I have my gun, anyway.
I follow him as he enters, careful,
Drawing his own revolver, smoke leaking
From his nostrils and forming white phantoms.

Through a second set of doors, we find him,
Sitting among science apparatus
Designed to measure the stars in some way.
His spectacles reflect the shining sky.

The Observatory is filled with things
That move: a map of our solar system,
And others of galaxies, and models
Of tides and stars and the places between.

Dante makes a path through the cluttered room,
Comes up to Norton with his revolver
Pointed straight at the man, but there's no need.
Norton doesn't stir, doesn't notice us.

Only when the cuffs click around his wrists
Does he move, dazed, puzzled, like we're strangers
Invading his home. 'What's happening here?'
'You're under arrest, sir.' 'For what?' 'For that.'

Norton sighs. He looks small, but still happy.
'Very well. Time to go, then, officers.'
Standing, with Dante holding his arms back,
Norton blinks quickly, his eyes adjusting.

'I suppose you have Magnusson,' he says.
I'm a way off, still near the entrance. 'No.'
'No?' 'Magnusson is dead. I shot him dead.'
'You killed him? Why?' 'He murdered Vivian.'

Bowing his head, Norton looks reproachful.
'Oh. I knew there were some casualties. But…'
'He never told you?' 'He… took care of things
While I designed the machines, the rocket.'

'But you suspected?' 'I suppose I did.'
I can't find it in myself to hate him.
Try as I might, I've got no anger left,
Only a sort of pity for the man.

Dante leads him across, and as he does,
I realise that Norton will be the one
Remembered for all the light in the sky.
He'll be famous for that, not for murder.

Before they can reach the door, something shines.
A pillar of glowing sweeps the stone floor
And we all pause, looking for the light's source.
The clouds have opened up for us at last.

I'm not expecting to see the colour
That appears between those retreating clouds.
I was imagining more white, maybe,
Or the usual blackness, but not blue.

More patches of blue emerge between clouds,
More shafts of light touching the dark city,
All visible through the great, domed glass roof.
I have to look away from the sun, though.

Free of the clouds, the sun has become fierce,
A dazzling white like nothing else I know,
As if every last light I've seen before
Has been no more than a spark when compared.

I shield my eyes and ask Norton, 'Why blue?'
'Because of our atmosphere,' he tells us,
'But does it matter?' I guess it doesn't.
It could have been any colour at all.

When we lead him into the parking lot,
There's a long parade of students waiting,
Whistling and cheering and clapping for him;
Such a celebration for the small man.

He remains humble, smiling, his head low,
Letting us guide him to the borrowed car
Where we left it hours back, waiting for us.
The students part, letting us pass between.

They're still there when we put him in the back,
Shutting the door behind him. He watches
His students and the sky from the window,
A sort of warm pride creasing his features.

I've got one act of generosity
Left in me this cycle, so I stop there,
Say to Dante, 'You take him in, Dante.
It's your turn. You take the credit for this.'

Dante glances around at the students,
And then to me. 'What are you gonna do?'
I shrug. 'Guess someone has to tell Cancer
What happened to his Heart. He won't be pleased.'

He leans against the car, hands me a smoke.
'You just don't want the fucking paperwork.'
I take the cigarette and ignite it,
Leaning with him and taking in the sky.
    The clouds are getting thinner and sparser,
Overwhelmed by all the brilliant blue.
I have to shield my eyes against the sun,
That bright beacon drowning the world in light.
    'You know how much I had for the Hangman?'
And it's the first time I've talked about it
With him, with anyone. 'It took a month.
They kept giving me more and more to write.'
    'Shit,' says Dante. 'Seriously? That much?'
'I swear I wrote the same report three times.'
'And that was just one man.' 'Yup. Only one.'
'I'm fucked, aren't I?' 'Sure as hell are, Dante.'
    We wait until the cigarettes are stubs
Before Dante searches for the car's keys
And thumps me on the shoulder. 'Good luck, Yorke.
Let's go for a drink when this is over.'
    'Sure,' I tell him, and that's enough for him.
He gets in and starts the engine, drives off,
Students cheering in his wake, bright faces
Reflecting the bright sun. I watch him go.

❯ • ❮

I stop and ask a stranger in the street,
'Got the time?' 'Sure,' he says. 'Twenty past ten.'
And I like the way the sunlight bounces
Off his watch: that timepiece become a star.

I take my time the rest of the way there,
In the knowledge that I'm already late,
Probably too late, and that I've missed her.
Hell, if she even remembered at all.

I find Vox's ghosts gathered in the park,
Hundreds and thousands of them sat staring
Upwards together, covering the ground;
Quiet bodies, quiet people, watching.

Even though it's warm, I pull my coat close
And make my way among them: countless ghosts,
Wasted forms as far as my eyes can see,
Some with fluttering fingers, clutching light.

This is one of the few places in Vox
The towers open up, leave a clear space
Wide enough to let the sky in, glowing
As it is right now, attracting the ghosts.

I wonder if any organised this,
Or if it was a wordless pilgrimage,
One following the other to the park
And filling it from gate to distant gate.

I pass spindly claw trees housing more ghosts,
Pale bodies sat in the upper branches
And reaching up, cupping their hands to catch
The sun, gather its bright light in their palms.

They don't seem to notice me as I go,
Stepping over them, hat pressed to my chest,
And I feel like the only living soul
Here, like I've come to the Garden of Phos.

Some of them are definitely dying
Or dead. I step across breathless bodies,
Some with wrists slit, some just wasted away,
And a few hanging by rope from the trees.

There's a bridge across a filthy brown stream
And I cross it, pushing past more bodies
And watching those ghosts stood in the water,
Letting the stream run around their ankles.

On the other side, I come to the hill
At the centre of the park, facing east,
Facing the sea, and from here I can see
The Lighthouse, Cancer's home, scratching the sky.

The ghosts here are sat shoulder to shoulder,
Glinting eyes wide to let in the sunlight,
Mouths wide as if they could almost drink it,
Some weeping freely, but all so silent.

I ascend the hill slowly, push through them,
To where, against all the odds, there's a bench
That's been left absent, ghosts sat around it
But not on it, like it was left for me.

And there, at the top of the hill, I sit
And watch the sun with them, getting duller.
The blue above begins to look less blue
As I wait, the dark returning at last.

I lean back, hat on my lap, and wonder
If Rachel wanted to meet to confess,
Or just because she wanted to see me,
Or for some other reason I don't know.

Running one hand across my scar, I know
It doesn't matter any more. Not now.
I'm too late. I wonder if she came here,
Crossed the sea of ghosts, to sit where I am.

The stillness in the park is infectious.
I get caught up in the calm, the quiet,
Find my thoughts turning to the shining sun,
My palms turned up like I could catch the light.

I don't know how much time passes sat there,
Only that the brightness in the sun fades
And the wind rises, pushing the vague clouds
Faster in white streaks across the deep blue.

At once, almost like it's a ritual,
I take my hands and run them down my face
As if I'm trying to push all the light
Collected between them into myself.

And when I lower them, there's someone sat
Beside me, who I mistake for Rachel
Until I turn my head to see Shepherd
Sat there instead, the scar on his face bright.

'You've come to kill me, then,' I say to him,
But he turns to me. 'Not this cycle, Yorke.'
'Then what?' 'I came to thank you for trying
To find the Heart. And because I like you.'

'You like me?' 'Sure I do. You remind me
Of me. It's like looking in a mirror.'
I don't think I agree, but I don't say.
I keep quiet, lean forwards, watch the sky.

The stars are starting to come out again.
In among the blue are a few bright points
Scattered here and there as tiny beacons,
Winking one by one back into vision.

The sun itself is starting to sink down,
Becoming bearable to look at straight,
Losing its glow, its sheen, its awesome shine,
Reverting back into its old dark self.

When I lean back again, Shepherd is gone.
In his place is a brown paper package
That glows slightly. I glance at it, then up,
And then across to the distant Lighthouse.

There's another star, a point of bright light
Glowing at the very top of its spire,
And I frown, wondering what it could be,
What it is that Cancer's doing up there.

For a while longer, I wait for Rachel.
The ghosts seem to start to gather closer,
Holding on to each other for comfort,
Confronted by the return of their hell.

It's my hell too, I realise. The dark
Come back again after a brief reprieve.
And it's not just the light above fading,
But the light in me, as well. I feel dark.

I take the package, put it in my bag
And stand, placing my hat upon my head.
This time, when I make my way through the ghosts,
I don't need to push. They part, let me pass.

> • <

When I reach the Lighthouse, the sky is red,
Like someone's stabbed the sun and made it bleed.
I stop before the doors and stare at it,
Watch the stars piercing the rising darkness.
   Above, at the top of the tall building,
I can see that same illumination.
This close, I can see orange flickering,
Causing lengthy shadows across the glass.
   There's a weight in my chest, a heaviness
That makes my ascent up to the front doors
Difficult, like my boots are made of lead.
Still, I stamp every step, remove my hat.
   At the top, I find the dark doors ajar,
Revealing the blackened interior.
The inside of the Lighthouse looks empty,
Like everyone, all the staff, have gone home.
   When I call out and knock, nobody comes.
My voice echoes around the dark inside,
Coming back to me. 'Hello?' I call. 'Hey?'
I push one of the doors aside, step in.

From what little light there is left outside,
I can see that the huge place is a mess.
Someone's smashed every single piece of glass,
Dropped the chandeliers, shattered all the bulbs.

    It's a beautiful disaster, the glass
Reflecting the red sky a thousand times,
Turning the whole huge entrance hall scarlet
And making the weight in me heavier.

    I push glass aside with my boots, ascend
The wide staircase and try to find Cancer.
And even though I know where he'll be,
I take my time, searching every side room.

    Everything is red from the sky outside,
And the story is the same: more smashed glass.
Whoever broke the Lighthouse broke it all,
Making sure that nothing was left untouched.

    It must take me the best part of an hour
To get close to the top, to the glass roof
Where once, according to Cancer, was lit
A torch bright enough to ward off star-ships.

    I find myself slowing, the flickering
Coming from above heralding a scene
I can predict. But still, I want to see,
I want to know what it is Cancer's done.

    Even though there won't be any answer,
I call out again, rounding the last bend
In the wide stairway, crunching across glass
Reflecting red and the orange glowing.

And there he is, Mister Cancer, bleeding
From what's left of his skull, gun still in hand,
Sat in a chair along one balcony,
Unseeing eyes watching the fading sun.

    Beside him is the source of the glowing.
It's a black chandelier filled with candles,
I count six, all lit and shining brightly,
Wavering softly, orange in the dark.

    I join him on the balcony. The sun
Is nearly gone now, no more than a smudge
Of crimson against the black, our dark star
Turning dark once again, all light leaving.

    From my bag, I find the Heart replica
And place it gently in Cancer's free hand,
Making sure he's got a tight grip on it
And removing the gun from his other.

    I weigh it in my hand, a heavy piece,
Still loaded. I press it against my skull.
Then, in one motion, I throw it away,
Send it spinning over the balcony.

    Instead, I move a chair beside Cancer
And rest myself on it, remove my coat
And try to work out what it was he saw
Up there in the sky when he killed himself.

    I roll my sleeve up and watch the last light
Vanish from the sky, the last bit of red,
That blushing, fragile, smiling, crimson red,
As it fades and turns back to a blackness.

I take my belt and wind it round my arm,
Flexing my fist and biting the leather,
Tightening it until I can see veins,
Making the loop complete, dividing me.

The brown paper bag contains three needles,
But one is enough, glowing with pale light.
I hold the needle tight between my teeth
And stare at the sun until it's gone black.

Then, at that moment, by the needle's light,
I find that bulging vein and puncture it,
Pressing down on the plunger and forcing
The liquid light quickly into my veins.

I loosen the belt, find myself gasping,
The rush of the drug sudden, dizzying.
I watch as my dull veins begin to glow,
Only a low light, barely even there.

I have moments before the high hits me,
And I use them taking deep breaths of air,
Filling my lungs with the city's darkness.
I can hear weeping and wailing below.

The city has returned to its darkness,
But not me. I found a way to escape.
The high hits me and I'm made of glowing.
I can feel the light coursing through my veins.

The candles are no more than little stumps,
Mostly burned away and looking ancient.
I run my hand through the small, orange flames,
Watch them dance and gush around my fingers.

There's an old legend told about candles,
That if you blow one out, you get a wish.
I take a deep breath and blow them all out,
Fragile flames gone, and I don't make a wish.

❯ • ❮

'Virgil!' She sounds scared, so I sprint to her,
Almost tripping over labelled boxes
And scattered bits of brand-new furniture
To get through to her in the dining room.
'What? What is it?' She's lit the bulb in here,
And by it we can see the wooden beams
Crossing the ceiling. She points up at one
That looks scarred, like someone's been chewing it.
I take a breath and fetch the stepladder,
Squeeze her hand before climbing it to see.
I was right, something has been eating it.
'Woodworm,' I tell her. 'But they're long gone now.'
'The ceiling's not gonna fall in?' she asks.
I laugh, smile and put my arms around her.
'It won't. Don't worry. You're safe here with me.'
She kisses me at the edge of my chin.

May Phos shine upon you
Illustration by Darren Kerrigan

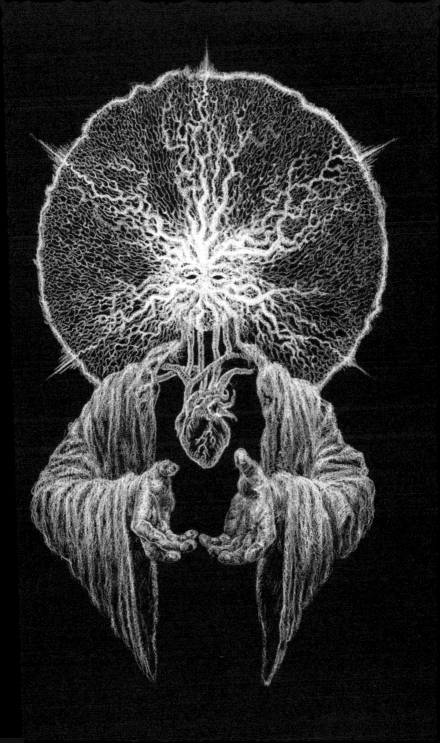

ACKNOWLEDGEMENTS

With thanks to:
Kirsty Gunn
James Stewart
Robert Dinsdale
George Sandison